GEMS OF NATURE
BIRDS
A SPECIES GUIDE

Mark E. Hauber is a graduate of Yale and Cornell Universities, and currently serves as the Harley Jones Van Cleave Professor of Host-Parasite Interactions in the Department of Evolution, Ecology, and Behavior at the University of Illinois/Urbana-Champaign.

He thanks Mehmet Caglar Kaya and Andy Suarez for supporting this project.

First published in the UK in 2021 by
Ivy Press
An imprint of The Quarto Group
The Old Brewery, 6 Blundell Street
London N7 9BH, United Kingdom
T (0)20 7700 6700
www.QuartoKnows.com

Material in this book was first published in 2014 in *The Book of Eggs*

British Library Cataloguing-in-Publication Data
A catalogue record for this book is available from
the British Library

ISBN: 978-0-7112-5843-3

This book was designed and produced by
Ivy Press
58 West Street, Brighton BN1 2RA, UK

Publisher David Breuer
Editorial Director Tom Kitch
Art Director James Lawrence
Commissioning Editor Kate Shanahan
Project Editor Joanna Bentley
Design Manager Anna Stevens
Designer Ginny Zeal
Map Artwork Richard Peters

Printed in Singapore

10 9 8 7 6 5 4 3 2 1

GEMS OF NATURE
BIRDS
A SPECIES GUIDE

MARK E. HAUBER

Ivy Press

CONTENTS

INTRODUCTION

Birds are some of the most colorful and melodious occupants of nature and, with more than 10,000 species on our planet, the amazing diversity of avian life around us easily captures the human imagination. Perhaps because people, much like birds, communicate with mostly sight and sound, we often feel a special connection with the avian companions in our lives, whether it is a pet parrot at home, or an overwintering robin in the local park. Specifically, watching bright and colorful birds at home and away both calms and alerts our senses; and bird songs can remind us of the promise of harmony and peace in the world surrounding us. This book brings you a visual taste of the diversity that exists across the avian world.

Birds and humans also share many other aspects of their daily lives: none closer perhaps than our similarities in family concepts. Most species provide biparental care for the young: even if the males and females differ in their roles and relative contributions, the majority of birds, like modern humans, live in nuclear families of a mother, a father, and their young. The exceptions to this rule are also fascinating: birds can form vast colonies of city-like nesting habitats, several overlapping generations can cooperate in raising the next brood of new progeny, and single-parent families, led by either a solitary mother or father, are also present in several avian lineages.

Finally, this unique group of modern-day dinosaurs also provides the human imagination with goals that we can hardly achieve: as one of the handful of animal lineages that have independently evolved the ability of flight, fluttering warblers and sparrows within the foliage of a tree and flocks of flying geese and cranes remind us of what we are missing in our daily experiences by living a mostly two-dimensional, pedestrian life. In turn, birds offer scientists much to study because avian species can accomplish feats that few other animal lineages can: they can fly over the oxygen-poor atmosphere of the highest peaks of the Himalayas on their way to and from the wintering and breeding grounds, or dive hundreds of meters deep into the total darkness of the ocean in search of elusive prey. Some birds even converged with bats not only in their abilities to sniff out nocturnal food sources but also to echolocate in deep caves with low light levels.

Let the birds highlighted in this volume take flight with you and your aspirations.

THE EVOLUTION OF BIRDS

Scientists now accept that birds are a specialized subgroup of one branch of dinosaurs, the therapods. While dinosaurs flourished into many different niches of life throughout the Cretaceous, some therapods evolved features allowing them to fly. Archaeopteryx, dating to about 150 million years ago, combined reptile features (teeth, clawed fingers, and a long tail) with wings and flight feathers resembling those of extant (living) birds. While this well-known fossil is no longer considered to be a direct ancestor of modern birds, many other bird fossils show that the earliest forms were small, perhaps arboreal, and able to glide. Modern birds likely evolved their diverse flight behaviors from this origin.

By 100 million years ago, the two major groups of modern birds had split from each other. Based on differences in their skulls, the Paleognathes ("old jawed birds") include the flightless ostriches, rheas, cassowaries, emus, kiwis, and the extinct elephantbirds and moas, as well as the flighted tinamous; the Neognathes ("new jaws") include the rest of the birds we know today. By the end of the Eocene, about 34 million years ago, all of the modern bird orders (and many of the extant families) roamed and flew in the diverse habitat of our ever-changing planet as members of distinct and recognizable lineages.

Which came first: the chicken or the egg?

This age-old question is an easy one to answer: the egg. Why? An egg is simply a reproductive cell, and animals (including the dinosaurs, the direct ancestors of modern birds) were laying eggs, including the hard-shelled, calcareous eggs of crocodilians and modern birds, for millions of years before the first fowl-like bird evolved. Of course, few non-avian eggs (then or now) looked like modern birds' eggs: with a soft membrane and no hard casing in some cases, they can be transparent, gelatinous, and quick to dry out. Most must remain in or near water in order for the young to develop and hatch.

Birds' eggs are "amniotic," meaning they contain features, including a hard shell and porous membranes, that allow them to be laid and develop on dry land. In the evolution of biodiversity on Earth, the appearance of the amniotic egg made possible a major habitat shift: animals could leave water in order to reproduce. This trait helped amniotes—reptiles, dinosaurs, birds, and mammals —to become a dominant form of animal life on Earth.

Packaging life

Why is it that all birds, large and small, put their entire future (embryo, hormones, antibiotics, vitamins, and lipids) into a fragile egg-package?

Humans and the majority of other mammals retain their fertilized eggs inside their bodies, where the developing young receive the nourishment and protection they need to grow directly from the mother. In contrast, a female bird packages everything that is needed to form a chick into her egg—and then ejects the egg from her body. Outside, the parent or parents must provide the warmth, shelter, and protection, typically in a nest, that the eggs need so that the embryos can fully develop and hatch into viable chicks.

Amongst the stories included in this book, many highlight the vast array of strategies and choices birds make to find appropriate mates and nesting sites, to warm and protect the eggs, and to assure adequate food, water, and shelter for the chicks. In particular, while the egg itself provides much that the embryo needs, the parents must still provide critical services. Typically, one or both parents provide the external heat necessary to jumpstart embryonic metabolism, and maintain the necessary microclimate, including high levels of humidity, to keep the eggs from desiccating. They select nest sites and build or usurp nests for the eggs to shield them from predators, sun, dryness, and other threats. They also rotate the eggs in the nest to assure even heating or cooling, and to prevent embryonic malformation.

The diversity of birds that successfully reproduce via the egg is astonishing. Birds live on every continent and successfully breed in every terrestrial habitat. In the frigid Antarctic where winter temperatures are below minus 40 degrees (both C and F) and wind speeds may reach 200 miles (over 320 km) per hour, the male Emperor Penguin stands in place, carrying its single egg on top of its feet in a feather-protected pouch for two months to warm it before the chick hatches. In Chile, Gray Gulls breed in the world's driest deserts, where few predators can venture to threaten the ground nests; the eggs and chicks are thus safe, but the parents must commute daily to large bodies of water to obtain food and moisture for themselves and their offspring.

Because of the hard shell, the egg must be fertilized while it is still inside the female's body, before the shell has formed. The chicken's ability to lay eggs, whether they are fertilized or not, accounts in part for its eggs being such an important food staple for humans across continents and cultures.

Size matters

In general, larger birds lay larger eggs; they also have thicker shells, which makes mechanical sense, with each egg having to withstand some of the weight of the incubating adult sitting on top of it. The ostrich's egg is the largest and heaviest of any living bird: weighing in at over 4 lb (2 kg), it represents more than 30 chicken-egg equivalents. At the other end of the scale, the smallest eggs are laid by hummingbirds; they are 1/5,000th the size of an ostrich egg and may weigh less than a paper clip. But when considered in relation to adult body weight, egg sizes tell a different story. In this context, ostrich eggs are rather small for the adult's weight and hummingbird eggs are rather large. Some of the largest eggs of any bird relative to the female's body weight are laid by several of the flightless kiwi species of New Zealand.

Thus, relative egg size, compared to adult body weight, is far from constant and varies extensively with ecology and evolutionary history. For example, birds that lay larger clutches also tend to lay smaller eggs, and species whose chicks hatch fully feathered and ready to follow the parents, tend to produce larger eggs than species whose chicks hatch blind and naked and require prolonged parental care. An egg's size varies with its internal content, which is controlled by the mother's strategy to provision the eggs with resources, including lipids in the yolk, and the concentrations of hormones, vitamins, and maternal antibodies in the yolk and the albumin.

NESTS

As a follow up to the set of successful reproductive strategies from which the egg originated, birds have also evolved an extraordinary array of structures to shelter, protect, and help warm the eggs and chicks: the nest.

The simplest definition of the nest is any structure or space that surrounds and houses the egg(s). Constructed nests are a form of tool use by animals: birds take materials found in the environment (including human castoffs), manipulate and modify them, and generate a novel use and function. This basic definition of tool use covers most bird nests, from the loose stick nest of a feral Rock Dove breeding on a window ledge, to the hundred-unit nesting aggregations of colonially breeding Sociable Weavers.

Enclosed nests, whether constructed as domes or within the cavity of a tree, keep the eggs and chicks out of the sight of predators and away from sun and rain. Building a nest in a hidden place, among dense tufts of grasses or foliage, ensures that discovery by competitors, and many nest predators, is minimized. A tight or difficult-to-access nest can also provide protection from parasites: Yellow Warblers, for example, protect their clutch by sitting tightly on the nest, so that the contents are not accessible to brood parasitic Brown-headed Cowbirds attempting to lay their eggs into the nest cup.

Finally, nesting sites and nests themselves can serve as an aphrodisiac; in many bird species, males attract females to their territory by building a nest or defending a nest site. Females choose a male based on his ability to build a sturdy nest in a safe location;

these traits of the nest architecture and location work together to assure greater reproductive success for both the talented male and the choosy female.

Hatching eggs without nests

Not all birds use a nest; some simply deposit the eggs on bare ground, a cliff ledge, in leaf litter, at the bottom of a tree cavity, or in a shallow ground scraping. Nevertheless, the heat for embryogenesis is still provided by the incubating adult. Many seabirds, including Australasian Gannets and Emperor Penguins, cannot afford to lose feathers from the chest to develop a barren skin area, called the brood patch, because they need to keep diving deep into the cold seawater for fish throughout the nesting period; in these cases, the heat is transferred to the eggs in other ways, particularly through the warm blood carried in the veins of the webbed feet.

Most unusually, brush turkeys and their relatives in the Galliform family of Megapodidae lay their eggs into heaping mounds of rotting vegetation or warm sandy soils near sunbathed beaches or volcanic slopes. There, the biochemical, solar, or geothermal energy provides the heat for the eggs to sustain embryonic development.

BREEDING STRATEGIES

Clutch size is the number of eggs a bird lays in one nesting attempt; it varies across species, from a single egg to as many as 20. In part, this is determined by evolutionary history; all albatrosses lay just one egg, hummingbirds consistently lay two, while partridges and quail can lay 10–15 or more. But this is not always the case. Clutch size can also vary within species, within populations, and even for an individual from year to year, based on such variables as habitat, latitude, altitude, nest type, size of a nesting colony, food availability, and body size and health of the mother. Such trade-offs and the choices involved are a critical part of a bird's breeding strategies at all levels, commonly termed as their "life history" traits.

Clutch size

Broadly speaking, natural selection leads birds to lay as many eggs as they can successfully rear. For example, birds that breed in northern latitudes tend to have larger clutches while related birds from the tropics lay fewer eggs; although temperate regions have a shorter breeding season, there is plenty of food during that time to feed more chicks. Birds that lay multiple clutches each year may have fewer eggs in their final clutches; this may be due to running out of resources by the mother but also could be related to the lesser availability of food later in the breeding season. Likewise, birds with precocial young (those that leave the nest soon after hatching and can feed themselves thereafter) lay more eggs per clutch than those with altricial young (those that require prolonged brooding and care).

Most small birds lay one egg each day until their clutch is complete; others, typically large birds, lay only one egg or lay consecutive eggs two to three days apart. Female kiwis, whose eggs can weigh some 25 percent of their body weight, may go weeks between laying the first and second egg.

Survival of the fittest

Parent birds can control to a certain extent the rate and timing of embryonic development inside the egg to influence the success of their breeding attempt. Some start to incubate each egg on the day when it is laid, resulting in asynchronous hatching; the chicks hatch over a series of days, and the first-hatched chicks are larger and more dominant. In Cattle Egrets, asynchronous hatching is taken further by the mother depositing different amounts of testosterone into the egg yolk: the first two eggs receive nearly twice as much as the last, third-laid egg. The result is that in seasons with poor food supplies, the hungry, aggressive, and large first chicks attack, peck, and drive off the small and timid last chick, often expelling it from the nest and assuring that the resulting brood of just two chicks receives sufficient food from the parents to fledge successfully.

In contrast, synchronous hatching takes place when the parents wait for all the eggs to be laid and start incubation on the last day, so that each egg hatches within hours of the others. This might assure equal chances of survival to more of the young.

Brood parasitism

Given what we know about the demands placed on bird parents, it is, perhaps, no surprise, that some bird lineages have evolved, independently of each other, to forgo most of the costs and hassles involved with parental care. Brood parasitism is a breeding strategy where eggs are laid into another bird's nest; the foreign eggs are then incubated by the foster-parent(s), who also feed and protect the parasitic young until they become fully independent. The effect of brood parasitism, as in all types of parasitism, is the loss of reproductive success for the host: foster-parents raising parasites misdirect expensive parental care to a genetically foreign young instead of their own progeny. In turn, the benefit of parasitism is to increase the number of their offspring produced by parasites, without the expense of full-term parental care.

Giving up on parenting

Most brood parasitic young represent more than a fair challenge for the foster-parents: nestling cowbirds and whydahs beg more intensively than their nest mates, and receive a more than equitable share of the parental food deliveries. This then typically causes the smaller and younger host nestlings to starve and perish in the parasitized brood. Nestlings of the Common Cuckoo and Greater Honeyguide go a step further. They eliminate all host eggs and nestlings soon after they themselves hatch; they toss host eggs and nestlings beyond the rim of the nest, or slaughter the host chicks with their sharply hooked beaks, respectively. The end result is that these chicks grow up alone in the nest, monopolizing all parental food deliveries.

A host-parasite arms-race

Clearly, both parasitism and antiparasitic strategies represent strong enough evolutionary forces to drive the counter-evolution of behavioral and morphological traits of both hosts and parasites. The result is a co-evolutionary arms-race process: hosts evolve to combat parasites, parasites evolve to evade the hosts, the hosts become better tuned to detect parasitism, and the parasites overcome the increasingly sophisticated host defenses. The best example of such a co-evolutionary process is the mimetic eggs of different host races of the Common Cuckoo, each specializing on one of the cuckoo's many host species: in this system, a female cuckoo lays a specific type of egg which best matches the colors and maculation patterns acceptable to the respective host. Often, the mimicry is so close that neither the host, nor the researcher, can tell the difference until the cuckoo chick hatches in the nest, and starts tossing the other eggs and chicks from the brood.

However, potential hosts have evolved several traits to reduce or eliminate parasitism. Many species aggressively defend their nests against intruding parasites, and loudly mob, even physically attack, them to prevent parasitism from occurring in the first place; some species have also evolved the ability to assess, discriminate, and reject imperfectly mimetic foreign eggs and chicks from the nest, piercing or grasping the parasite's egg and tossing it out of the nest. Other host species listen to the begging calls produced by their own chicks and refuse to feed nestlings that sound different from their own.

About this book
The species represented in this book are grouped as follows:
Water birds, including ducks, geese, loons, and herons
Large non-passerine land birds, including ostriches and birds of prey
Small non-passerine land birds, including cuckoos, hummingbirds, and woodpeckers
Passerine "perching birds," including flycatchers, jays, warblers, sparrows, blackbirds, and finches.

Accompanying the colorful illustration of each bird is a map showing its breeding range, a summary of its breeding habitat, nest type and placement, and its current conservation status. The range of measurements is given for the average adult size.

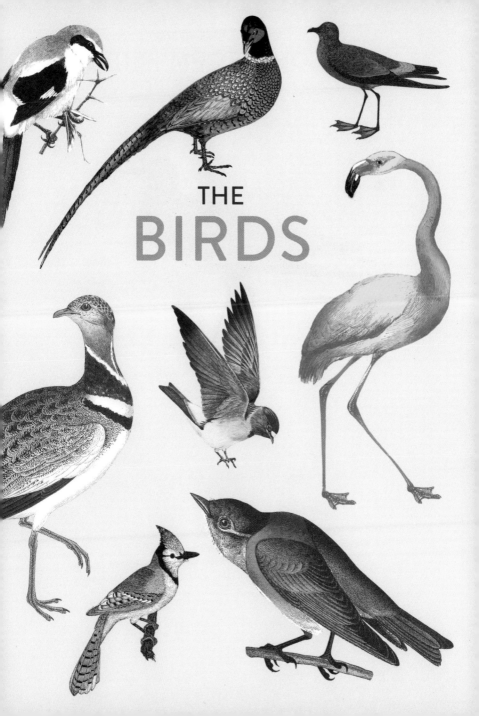

THE
BIRDS

WILSON'S STORM-PETREL

PROCELLARIIFORMES

ADULT BIRD SIZE RANGE
6⅓–7⅓ in (16–19 cm)

ORDER ~ Procellariiformes

FAMILY ~ Oceanitidae

BREEDING RANGE ~ Antarctic coastline, subantarctic islands

BREEDING HABITAT ~ Oceanic shores, rocky or grassy plateaus

NEST TYPE AND PLACEMENT ~ Rock crevices and ground burrows, near the sea

CONSERVATION STATUS ~ Least concern

Unlike other storm-petrels, this species flies with less flutter and in more direct lines. Strictly pelagic during the non-breeding season, it can be seen in the North Pacific and Atlantic but it breeds predominantly on the shores of Antarctica and its islands.

The thin legs of the Wilson's Storm-Petrel make walking on land difficult and so the species breeds near cliffs facing the ocean, often in large colonies. Late spring snowstorms may interfere with its ability to leave or access the nest, causing breeding failure. The parents do not come to land for nesting during the daytime or even on clear-lit nights, in order to avoid attracting the attention of larger birds intent on preying on the adults or their eggs and chicks. In the darkness, individuals use a keen sense of smell to relocate their own nesting burrows, mates, and chicks.

The Wilson's Storm-Petrel is a small pelagic seabird, with characteristic white rump against its dark plumage, long legs, and yellow, webbed feet. It uses both fluttering and gliding flight to collect food from the ocean's surface.

DISTRIBUTION

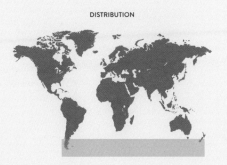

APTENODYTES PATAGONICUS

KING PENGUIN

SPHENISCIFORMES

ADULT BIRD SIZE RANGE
35–37 in (90–94 cm)

ORDER ~ Sphenisciformes

FAMILY ~ Spheniscidae

BREEDING RANGE ~ Remote subantarctic islands in the Southern Ocean

BREEDING HABITAT ~ Muddy or rocky flats near the beach

NEST TYPE AND PLACEMENT ~ No nest; the egg is carried inside a brood pouch between the feet

CONSERVATION STATUS ~ Least concern

This is the second largest penguin species, exceeded only by the Emperor Penguins of Antarctica. Both sexes display colorful facial and neck feathers providing cues for recognizing individuals in the large colonies, which can number in the hundreds of thousands to millions of birds. Individuals with brighter facial feathering have better mating success in this species.

The breeding cycle of this penguin is highly variable. A typical spring-summer-fall cycle starts when eggs are laid in the early spring, and ends in fall with the chick reaching 90 percent of the adult weight, at which point the parents leave it. But if egg laying is delayed to late spring, the cycle can take up to 14 months: one of the longest reproductive cycles of any bird. Once the egg hatches, and the chick is a month old, parents leave them in crèches (avian kindergartens) where a select few adults look after the young, while most parents head out to sea to fish for their own young's next meal.

The King Penguin is a colonial breeder of the subantarctic islands and, recently, of mainland South America itself. Its distinctive dark and light patterned plumage is ornamented by oranges and yellows around the breast and neck.

DISTRIBUTION

GAVIA IMMER

COMMON LOON

GAVIIFORMES

MALE

FEMALE

ADULT BIRD SIZE RANGE
26–36 in (66–91 cm)

ORDER ~ Gaviiformes

FAMILY ~ Gaviidae

BREEDING RANGE ~ North America landmasses and islands of the
North Atlantic

BREEDING HABITAT ~ On shores of lakes, preferring to nest on islands

NEST TYPE AND PLACEMENT ~ Bulky ground nest made up of twigs, grasses, reeds,
and dried water plants

CONSERVATION STATUS ~ Least concern

Agile in the water, loons are awkward and slow-moving on land. The Common Loon, or Great Northern Loon or Diver, prefers to nest on islands in lakes to keep both itself and its eggs safe from ground predators. Nevertheless, many nests are destroyed when Arctic Foxes or raccoons swim out to the islands, or avian predators including gulls and jaegers (skuas) attack from the air.

The parents are highly territorial and keep others of their own species off the waters of their breeding lakes. Once the chicks hatch, they are mobile and able to swim within a day, but they rely on their parents to feed them small prey for several weeks before they develop into efficient fish hunters. The typically two chicks hatch 24 hours apart, and quickly establish an age- and size-based hierarchy. In years when the parents cannot bring enough food to their chicks, only the alpha young survives to independence.

The Common Loon is a heavy-set, aquatic bird, with its feet positioned far back in the body to provide propulsion during its fishing dives. Its breeding plumage features glossy black and white patterns. Non-breeding birds are pale gray with a white collar.

DISTRIBUTION

PODICEPS NIGRICOLLIS

EARED GREBE

PODICIPEDIFORMES

ADULT BIRD SIZE RANGE
12–14 in (30–35 cm)

ORDER – Podicipediformes

FAMILY – Podicipedidae

BREEDING RANGE – Every continent, except Australia, South America, and Antarctica

BREEDING HABITAT – Swamps and lakes with dense vegetation

NEST TYPE AND PLACEMENT – A mound of plant matter on emergent plants in shallow water or directly in the lake shore vegetation

CONSERVATION STATUS – Least concern

Also known as the Black-necked Grebe, this species is socially monogamous, with both the female and male actively involved in building the nest, incubating the eggs, and looking after the young. Nesting in loose, but occasionally large, colonies of several hundred individuals, the family quickly leaves the nest after hatching. The chicks can swim and dive, but cannot fish at hatching, so the parents provision their young by feeding them small fish from beak to beak.

At about ten days of age the parents may split the brood, and lead each half separately for the rest of the three-week period before the chicks finally fledge. Such "brood divisioning" occurs in many birds with dependent young, and is thought to reduce the risk of losing all the young due to predation of one or both of the parents or all the young if they remain together.

The Eared Grebe is a relatively small grebe, but distinctive with its brightest and darkest feather coloration during the breeding season, and its striking red eye set against a black and rusty head plumage.

DISTRIBUTION

PHOENICOPTERUS RUBER

AMERICAN FLAMINGO

PHOENICOPTERIFORMES

ADULT BIRD SIZE RANGE
47–57 in (120–145 cm)

ORDER ~ Phoenicopteriformes

FAMILY ~ Phoenicopteridae

BREEDING RANGE ~ Islands and continental shores of the Caribbean, Galapagos

BREEDING HABITAT ~ Mudflats, lagoons, coastal lakes

NEST TYPE AND PLACEMENT ~ Ground nest a crater of built-up mud, standing in shallow water

CONSERVATION STATUS ~ Least concern

The only flamingo native to North America, this charismatic and conspicuous species relies on the safety of large flocks and hard-to-access breeding sites, rather than weaponry or aggression, to defend its nest. Crowded colonial life is so essential for the American Flamingo that zookeepers have been able to induce small groups of captive flamingos to nest and breed successfully by playing back sounds of large numbers of birds recorded at vast colonies.

The success of the American Flamingo's strategy of feeding and breeding on remote mudflats and lagoons has allowed them to maintain population sizes despite laying just a single egg per year. Some individuals can survive to more than 40 years of age, assuring that at least a handful of those breeding attempts will yield a viable chick to recruit for the next generation.

The American Flamingo is a tall and thin bird with deep orange and pink coloration typical of its relatives, too. When the flocks take flight in unison, the black-tinged wingtip feathers become clearly visible.

DISTRIBUTION

CYGNUS COLUMBIANUS

TUNDRA SWAN

ANSERIFORMES

ADULT BIRD SIZE RANGE
47–59 in (120–150 cm)

ORDER ~ Anseriformes

FAMILY ~ Anatidae

BREEDING RANGE ~ Arctic and subarctic tundra in Eurasia and
North America

BREEDING HABITAT ~ Pools, ponds, and lakes across coastal plains

NEST TYPE AND PLACEMENT ~ The bulky nest is placed on the ground on a mound
or ridge, built up from grasses and leaves, with little
down lining

CONSERVATION STATUS ~ Least concern

This is a large and common swan species; taxonomists currently consider that two races of Tundra Swan—the European Bewick's Swan and the American Whistling Swan—are separate from each other only at the subspecies level. Generally flocking during the winter and spending the nights floating on open water, in the reproductive season these swans pair off, defend breeding ranges against other swans and most other species happening to approach the nest, and sleep on solid ground near their nest.

Like many geese, but few duck species, both female and male swans are devoted to the prolonged duties and many costs of parental care; they only leave the nest when predators large enough to prey on the adults approach. These include wolves, bears, and of course, people.

The Tundra Swan in the American Arctic has a mostly black bill and a body feathered in pure white, while the European race has a large yellow patch at the base of the beak.

DISTRIBUTION

SPATULA CLYPEATA

NORTHERN SHOVELER

ANSERIFORMES

ADULT BIRD SIZE RANGE
17–20 in (44–51 cm)

ORDER ~ Anseriformes

FAMILY ~ Anatidae

BREEDING RANGE ~ Arctic and temperate North America and Eurasia

BREEDING HABITAT ~ Shallow grassy marshes, with thick layers of
bottom mud

NEST TYPE AND PLACEMENT ~ Simple ground scrape, surrounded by vegetation
on at least three sides, placed near open water

CONSERVATION STATUS ~ Least concern

This conspicuous and unique duck makes the most of its feeding specialization: a broad, spoon-shaped bill best suited to sifting through vast amounts of swamp water to filter and trap small aquatic invertebrates. Though laborious to collect, these foods provide more than sufficient protein supplies for the female to invest energy in forming and laying her eggs.

The female relies on her own nutrient reserves to provision the eggs with sufficient levels of fats to fuel embryonic development; with each gram of lipid deposited into an egg, a female loses 1/40 oz (0.75 g) of fat reserves stored during the wintering period. Because the males provide no energetic or material investment in the egg, their fat reserves remain stable during the breeding period. The female also bears the rest of the costs of parental care, both incubating the eggs and protecting the ducklings on her own.

The Northern Shoveler is most distinguishable by its large beak, black in the males and orange in the females. The breeding-season males also feature a tricolored plumage, including green, white, and rusty-red blocks of feathers.

DISTRIBUTION

BRANTA CANADENSIS

CANADA GOOSE

ANSERIFORMES

ADULT BIRD SIZE RANGE
30–43 in (75–110 cm)

ORDER ~ Anseriformes

FAMILY ~ Anatidae

BREEDING RANGE ~ Native to North America, introduced into Europe, New Zealand

BREEDING HABITAT ~ Open pastures, grassy fields, near water

NEST TYPE AND PLACEMENT ~ Ground nest of bulky dried vegetation and downy feathers

CONSERVATION STATUS ~ Least concern

34

This is a highly adaptable goose that appears to be as happy nesting in parks and other human-modified habitats as it does on the tundra of the high Arctic. These qualities have allowed Canada Geese to spread from their native ranges into more southern and urbanized regions of North America, and also to establish themselves firmly as invasive exotics in Europe and New Zealand.

The close association of large populations of these birds with humans—and the threat that airborne birds may pose to aircraft taking off and landing—has led to efforts to control their numbers by methods that include culling and disruption of nesting by shaking the eggs so that they will not hatch.

The Canada Goose is common and a familiar sight to people both in its native and introduced ranges, where its brownish body, stark black neck, and white chin-strap give it a unique appearance.

DISTRIBUTION

CLANGULA HYEMALIS

LONG-TAILED DUCK

ANSERIFORMES

ADULT BIRD SIZE RANGE
15–23 in (38–58 cm)

ORDER ~ Anseriformes

FAMILY ~ Anatidae

BREEDING RANGE ~ Arctic plains and coastal areas of North America,
Europe, and Asia

BREEDING HABITAT ~ Marshes and pools in the tundra, but also along
Arctic coastlines and mountain lakes

NEST TYPE AND PLACEMENT ~ Scrape in the ground, lined with leaves and padded
with down feathers; in loose colonies near the
water's edge, including on islands and peninsulas

CONSERVATION STATUS ~ Least concern

This is a unique duck, and not only because of the conspicuousness of its dark and light plumage patterns and the male's elongated central tail feathers. It is also the deepest-diving sea-duck, capable of spending much more time in search of invertebrates and fish at a depth of 200 ft (60 m) than the time needed to catch its breath on the surface between the dives.

The consortship between female and male Long-tailed Ducks ends at the start of incubation, and the mother looks after the young alone. Within a day the hatchlings are capable of feeding and diving unassisted. Still, early on, females dive with the young, dislodging food items that are then quickly captured and consumed by the ducklings.

The Long-tailed Duck is unmistakable, not only because of its prominent central tail feathers in males, but because its white/gray and black/brown plumages are shared between the sexes both during and outside the breeding season.

DISTRIBUTION

SOMATERIA MOLLISSIMA

COMMON EIDER

ANSERIFORMES

ADULT BIRD SIZE RANGE
19½–28 in (50–71 cm)

ORDER ~ Anseriformes

FAMILY ~ Anatidae

BREEDING RANGE ~ Northern North America, northern Europe,
and northeastern Siberia

BREEDING HABITAT ~ Coastal plains in the Arctic and subarctic

NEST TYPE AND PLACEMENT ~ A hollowed scrape in the ground, near the open
water; lined thickly with eiderdown plucked from
the female's own chest

CONSERVATION STATUS ~ Least concern

Common Eiders are highly social, both in the winter and on the breeding grounds. Females typically return from migration to the close vicinity of their natal nesting site, often to the same island where they themselves hatched. This phenomenon, called natal philopatry (returning to the original nesting site), and breeding site fidelity (returning by adult females to breeding sites each year) results in close relatives often nesting near one another. The benefits of close-kin associations include that females, which accept eggs laid by related females into their own nest, end up raising nieces and nephews instead of genetically unrelated chicks.

Perhaps the most famous colony of these eiders still exists in northern England, where, in 676 CE, St. Cuthbert enacted the first-known bird-protection laws to combat over-harvesting. About 1,000 pairs still nest in the same area today. This is one of the earliest known examples of conservation.

The Common Eider is a sexually dichromatic (differently colored) species in which males boast characteristically black and white feather plumages, whereas the females are strongly camouflaged by their brown hues displayed throughout their body.

DISTRIBUTION

CICONIA CICONIA

WHITE STORK

CICONIIFORMES

ADULT BIRD SIZE RANGE
39½–45½ in (100–115 cm)

ORDER ~ Ciconiiformes

FAMILY ~ Ciconiidae

BREEDING RANGE ~ Central and eastern Europe, western and central
Asia; reintroduced to western Europe. Locally in
South Africa

BREEDING HABITAT ~ Open grassy fields, marshes, and swamplands,
often near human settlements

NEST TYPE AND PLACEMENT ~ Large, bulky nests built on top of trees, lamp poles,
or chimneys, repaired and used repeatedly for years

CONSERVATION STATUS ~ Least concern

The White Stork in much of its distribution has become a strict commensalist of rural human settlements. These birds seek out nesting sites on top of chimneys and power poles, returning each year to the exact same site, to repair and reuse their nest, typically undisturbed by human neighbors and observers. Not only do these storks share their nesting habitat with people, the large, bulky stick nests also become homes for many other birds, including House Sparrows, which may build nests in the base of the storks' nest.

White Storks provided some of the earliest direct evidence of long migratory flights by birds. Specifically, during the spring of 1822, a stork returned to Europe with a traditional African hunting spear lodged firmly through its neck.

The White Stork is a long-legged and long-beaked bird, notable for its white and black plumage and bright red beak and legs. Flying with its neck and feet extended, it can be seen in large flocks during migration.

DISTRIBUTION

PLEGADIS FALCINELLUS

GLOSSY IBIS

PELECANIFORMES

ADULT BIRD SIZE RANGE
19–26 in (48–66 cm)

ORDER ~ Pelecaniformes

FAMILY ~ Threskiornithidae

BREEDING RANGE ~ Eastern North America, coastal Caribbean, Europe,
Southeast Asia, Africa, Pacific islands, Australia

BREEDING HABITAT ~ Marshes and wetlands

NEST TYPE AND PLACEMENT ~ Shallow stick and twig nest, lined with grasses, in low
bushes and trees

CONSERVATION STATUS ~ Least concern

This is the world's most widely distributed ibis species, occurring on all but one continents in both hemispheres. They nest in colonies with ibis of the same and different species, as well as herons and egrets. However, around the nest's vicinity, these ibis are highly aggressive and territorial. Both sexes incubate the eggs and feed the nestlings, changing guard over the eggs and small chicks following prolonged vocal displays to one another.

Incubation is asynchronous, which means that by the time the last laid egg hatches, the new chick is typically younger and smaller than its nest mates, which hatched earlier. Parents feed the chicks by regurgitating recently captured food and putting it directly into the beaks of the chicks. However, unlike the case in many heron nests, this ibis's young do not directly fight with each other, perhaps because the parents appear to preferentially feed the smallest chick in the nest first. Thus, parental control over their progeny, it appears, is complete in the Glossy Ibis.

The Glossy Ibis appears dark, nearly black, from a distance, but upon closer inspection, it displays a chestnut front and greenish iridescent wing feathers.

DISTRIBUTION

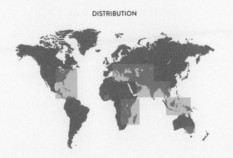

EGRETTA CAERULEA

LITTLE BLUE HERON

PELECANIFORMES

ADULT BIRD SIZE RANGE
22–29 in (56–74 cm)

ORDER ~ Pelecaniformes

FAMILY ~ Ardeidae

BREEDING RANGE ~ Temperate North America, Central and South
America, and the Caribbean

BREEDING HABITAT ~ Freshwater swamps, brackish lagoons, coastal
thickets and islands

NEST TYPE AND PLACEMENT ~ Platform nest of sticks, reeds, and grasses, in trees
and bushes; in colonies of mixed heron species

CONSERVATION STATUS ~ Least concern

Adult Little Blue Herons are dark blue, but young birds are pure white up to two years of age. Interestingly, the white plumage pattern of the young may have evolved and been maintained not just to reduce aggression from breeding adult conspecifics, but also to increase tolerance by other small, white wading birds, including Snowy Egrets. White-colored Little Blue Herons are tolerated more and capture more fish when next to Snowy Egrets, compared to older, dark-feathered individuals. The white plumage may also protect the young herons from predation, especially when roosting or flying together with other white herons and egrets.

When not stalking prey by standing still in shallow waters, this species can also follow farmers and livestock in fields and pastures, capturing small insects flushed by the equipment and the movement of a herd.

The Little Blue Heron is in fact an egret, belonging to the same genus as many white-colored egret species. During the breeding season, it displays long and filamentous purplish neck and head feathers.

DISTRIBUTION

PELECANUS OCCIDENTALIS

BROWN PELICAN

PELECANIFORMES

ADULT BIRD SIZE RANGE
39½–54 in (100–137 cm)

ORDER ~ Pelecaniformes

FAMILY ~ Pelecanidae

BREEDING RANGE ~ Coastal southern North America, the Caribbean,
Central America, and coastal South America

BREEDING HABITAT ~ Coastal and estuarine marshes

NEST TYPE AND PLACEMENT ~ Large stick and grass platform in short trees,
nests colonially

CONSERVATION STATUS ~ Least concern

Brown Pelicans nest in large colonies in coastal swamps, a habitat that is vulnerable to hurricanes, oil spills, and other natural and human-caused catastrophes. There, even in typical years, they face varying levels of food supplies. As a result, Brown Pelicans engage in facultative siblicide: chicks tolerate each other only when food is plentiful, but in food-poor years they fight to the death over scraps of fish brought by the parents.

The Brown Pelican, along with the Peregrine Falcon, is also a poster child for population recovery following the elimination of harmful pesticides in the larger ecosystem. Eggshell thinning caused by DDT led to the Brown Pelican being listed as endangered in the United States, even though its broad geographic distribution would have assured the survival of its populations elsewhere. Following the 1972 ban on DDT, its populations in the United States have made a dramatic recovery.

The Brown Pelican is an agile species that uses plunge-diving to trap fish in its gular pouch. The Atlantic and Pacific coast races vary in the intensity of red and yellow displayed on their heads.

DISTRIBUTION

BLACK-NECKED STILT

CHARADRIIFORMES

ADULT BIRD SIZE RANGE
14–15½ in (35–39 cm)

ORDER ~ Charadriiformes

FAMILY ~ Recurvirostridae

BREEDING RANGE ~ Southern North America, Central and northeastern South America, the Caribbean, Hawaii

BREEDING HABITAT ~ Freshwater ponds and coastal wetlands

NEST TYPE AND PLACEMENT ~ A scraped hollow in the ground, lined sparsely with twigs and pebbles, or not at all

CONSERVATION STATUS ~ Least concern, endangered subspecies in Hawaii

Like all stilts, the Black-necked Stilt has a distinctive look that includes a long straight beak and a curved neck, a strongly patterned black-and-white plumage, and incredibly thin, but long, legs. In fact, stilts are only second to flamingos when it comes to the relative length of these legs compared to the rest of the body and beak. Wading through shallow water, these birds are adept at capturing aquatic insects and other prey under the surface.

While foraging in flocks, many birds use sentries to watch for danger while the rest of the flock feeds. Stilts have evolved another defense mechanism: left and right sidedness in visual functions. They use their right eye to detect and reach for prey, and their left to spot predators and potential competitors or mates. This lateralization, much like handedness in humans, is controlled by different sides of the brain.

The Black-necked Stilt is a characteristically black and white bird with bright pink legs. The amount of black is highly variable both across the different age-classes of juvenile vs. adult birds, as well across its geographic range.

DISTRIBUTION

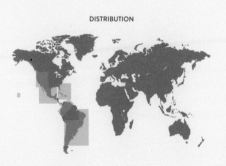

NORTHERN JACANA

CHARADRIIFORMES

ADULT BIRD SIZE RANGE
8½–9½ in (21–24 cm),
females are twice as heavy as males

ORDER ~ Charadriiformes

FAMILY ~ Jacanidae

BREEDING RANGE ~ Mexico and Central America, the Caribbean

BREEDING HABITAT ~ Wetlands, lakes, and rivers with floating vegetation

NEST TYPE AND PLACEMENT ~ A compact mound of pulled stems and leaves,
formed into a floating mat

CONSERVATION STATUS ~ Least concern

In common with all other jacanas, a female Northern Jacana keeps a harem of males. She mates with each in turn and can lay her eggs for the males all year long when water levels are stable. Each male incubates and tends to his own young. Polyandry, thus, frees the female from the cost of nest building, incubating, and protecting the young. She trades off parenting for increased egg production.

Jacanas live, feed, mate, and breed in marshes. They are poor fliers, and when they take to the wing, their flight is labored and their long legs and toes are simply dragged behind, dangling below the body. The Northern Jacana is called the "Jesus Bird" in Jamaica, because its long, thin toes and light body weight enable this bird to step across stems and leaves of floating vegetation, so appearing as if it can walk on water.

The Northern Jacana is a rusty-brown plumaged bird with a black neck and a yellow facial shield. Where it meets the Wattled Jacana in Panama, the two species hybridize, with the progeny displaying red and yellow wattles.

DISTRIBUTION

NUMENIUS AMERICANUS

LONG-BILLED CURLEW

CHARADRIIFORMES

ADULT BIRD SIZE RANGE
19½–25½ in (50–65 cm)

ORDER ~ Charadriiformes

FAMILY ~ Scolopacidae

BREEDING RANGE ~ Temperate central and western North America

BREEDING HABITAT ~ Open grasslands

NEST TYPE AND PLACEMENT ~ Shallow hollow, lined with grasses and weeds

CONSERVATION STATUS ~ Least concern

The impressively long, downward-curving beak of this large shorebird allows it to hunt for earthworms, crabs, and crickets hiding in long burrows. But these birds also probe mud, catch grasshoppers off plants, and even devour small lizards and other birds' eggs. Historically, this was a popularly hunted species; today, habitat destruction of prairie grasslands presents an ongoing threat for long-term population viability and the health of the Long-billed Curlew.

Nesting begins with the male scraping a hollow in the ground, and the female using her breast and bill to widen it. She then lines it with pebbles, dirt, and plant matter. Both parents incubate the eggs, with the female taking her turn during the day and the male during the night. Once the eggs hatch, both parents protect the young from predators, but the female typically abandons her mate and brood before the young reach independence.

The Long-billed Curlew is North America's largest and longest-billed shorebird species. Adult females are larger than males, but both sexes are cryptically colored with cinnamon-brown hues throughout their plumage.

DISTRIBUTION

ARENARIA INTERPRES

RUDDY TURNSTONE

CHARADRIIFORMES

ADULT BIRD SIZE RANGE
8½–10 in (21–26 cm)

ORDER ~ Charadriiformes

FAMILY ~ Scolopacidae

BREEDING RANGE ~ Northern coastlines of North America, Europe, and Asia

BREEDING HABITAT ~ Grassland and wetlands near the coastline, rocky Arctic shores

NEST TYPE AND PLACEMENT ~ Shallow scrape in the ground, lined with grass

CONSERVATION STATUS ~ Least concern

True to its name, the turnstone uses its wedge-shaped bill to pry between rocks and to move pebbles around as it searches for insects and crustaceans hiding in crevices. It also inspects and picks prey from the top of the sand and the surface of driftwood. This feeding strategy is highly adaptable and successful globally, and allows these birds to migrate around the globe, from the Arctic through temperate and tropical shores, and all the way south to Australia and New Zealand.

The male Ruddy Turnstone establishes his breeding territory early in the season, and attracts a female by consorting with her throughout the area. He ceremonially scrapes nest-shaped patches in the ground, and the potential pair inspect these scrapes together. Eventually, when the female decides on a mate, she builds and lines her own nest, away from all the male scrapes made during the courtship.

The Ruddy Turnstone is a blotchily plumaged, white-black-rusty patterned sandpiper. Its characteristic plumage becomes noticeably duller and grayer during the non-breeding season.

DISTRIBUTION

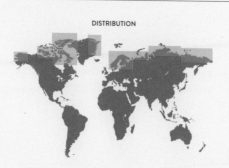

AMERICAN WOODCOCK

CHARADRIIFORMES

ADULT BIRD SIZE RANGE
10½–12 in (27–31 cm)

ORDER ~ Charadriiformes

FAMILY ~ Scolopacidae

BREEDING RANGE ~ Eastern North America

BREEDING HABITAT ~ Clearings in forests, shrubby areas near water

NEST TYPE AND PLACEMENT ~ Shallow ground nest of twigs and leaves, with brushy
or sapling cover

CONSERVATION STATUS ~ Least concern

The American Woodcock is a shorebird species which has taken to living in open woodland and adjacent fields in eastern North America. It is also one of the few wader-relatives that is still a commonly hunted game species; in the United States alone, around half a million woodcocks are shot each year.

Generally a well camouflaged species, male woodcocks put on quite a show to attract their mates each spring. They fly, zigzag, flutter, and make dives in midair, while calling and chirping to any nearby female on the ground. If the female likes this show, she flies directly in and lands nearby on the ground. The species is polygynous, and the male will continue his attempts to attract new females throughout the breeding season.

The American Woodcock is a cryptic and hard-to-notice species, except for its sounds and flights during the male's mate-attraction displays. The female's brown-patterned plumage provides her with effective camouflage for the incubation period.

DISTRIBUTION

ROSTRATULA BENGHALENSIS

GREATER PAINTED-SNIPE

CHARADRIIFORMES

ADULT BIRD SIZE RANGE
9–11 in (23–28cm)

ORDER ~ Charadriiformes

FAMILY ~ Rostratulidae

BREEDING RANGE ~ Sub-Saharan Africa, south and southwest Asia

BREEDING HABITAT ~ Wetlands, reed beds, near shores of ponds
and streams

NEST TYPE AND PLACEMENT ~ Shallow scrape in soft ground, lined with stems
and leaves, typically near water

CONSERVATION STATUS ~ Least concern

Painted-Snipes are not close relatives of "real" snipes. Like snipes, however, they use their long beaks to probe for aquatic prey, but their appearance is more like that of a typical wader, with long legs. The female is one of the most colorful shorebird species, sporting a rich chocolate brown plumage and distinctive chest bands, compared to the smaller and plainer, brown and striped male. As might be expected from this "reversed" sexual dimorphism, this species is polyandrous, with the female initiating courtship with the male, before she lays the eggs for him. Then she moves on to mate with another male.

The male provides all parental care of the eggs and chicks. He will lead chicks to feeding sites, and away from predators into dense vegetation. When threatened, the male also carries the chicks, tucking them under his wings as he moves away from danger.

The Greater Painted-Snipe is a reversed sexually dimorphic species, with the parental males displaying brown-patterned feathers, useful for crypsis during incubation, in contrast to the bright and contrastingly colored feather patches of the larger females.

DISTRIBUTION

STERNULA ANTILLARUM

LEAST TERN

CHARADRIIFORMES

ADULT BIRD SIZE RANGE
8½–9 in (21–23 cm)

ORDER ~ Charadriiformes

FAMILY ~ Laridae

BREEDING RANGE ~ Southern coasts and inland major river systems of North America

BREEDING HABITAT ~ Gravel or sandy beaches and coastlines on the sea, lakes, or rivers

NEST TYPE AND PLACEMENT ~ Ground scraping in the sand or gravel, occasionally on rooftops

CONSERVATION STATUS ~ Least concern

60

Least Terns prefer low-lying, sandy shores for nesting and breeding, which makes their greatest competitors none other than beach-going people. Habitat modification has thus negatively impacted seashore breeding colonies of this small tern species. Similarly, the inland populations that settle on small alluvial islands of slow-flowing rivers in North America have also been hurt by management to artificially alter water levels that coincides with the breeding season, and by the building up of river banks and construction of dams. Both of these activities interfere with the formation of temporary sand banks, further reducing the available nesting habitats for this species.

The eggs are highly variable in color and markings, often within the same clutch, possibly to enhance camouflage and crypsis. Perhaps because of this variation, the eggs are not individually recognized and parent terns readily retrieve and adopt eggs of other pairs nesting nearby.

The Least Tern is one of the small-bodied tern species that occur across Eurasia and South America. It can be recognized by its prominently patterned black and white facial features, and its solidly gray tail and rump.

DISTRIBUTION

GREAT SKUA

CHARADRIIFORMES ·

ADULT BIRD SIZE RANGE
19½–23 in (50–58 cm)

ORDER ~ Charadriiformes

FAMILY ~ Stercorariidae

BREEDING RANGE ~ Northern European coast and islands

BREEDING HABITAT ~ Coastal moorlands and rocky islets

NEST TYPE AND PLACEMENT ~ Ground nest on rocky coast or in fields,
lined with grasses

CONSERVATION STATUS ~ Least concern

The Great Skua is a large, bulky seabird, and it uses its size, rather than agility, to be successful on the breeding and wintering grounds. When it spots other birds—including gulls, terns, and even gannets—with freshly caught prey, it flies directly at them, pinches their wing in its beak, and follows the falling victim directly to the water, where it continues to attack it, unless the targeted species regurgitates its prey. This advanced form of kleptoparasitism complements the other food sources of skuas, which typically include fish, the eggs and chicks of other birds, and rodents.

Individual Great Skuas may become specialists, feeding solely on stolen food or only on fish. Specialization seems to pay off for these individuals, compared to generalist feeders, because the specialists start nesting earlier in the season, lay larger eggs, and raise faster-growing chicks.

The Great Skua is the least colorful of the northern hemisphere-breeding skua species, with a dull brown-patterned plumage covering its whole body. Its kleptoparasitic feeding habits are enhanced, however, by its sharp and hooked beak.

DISTRIBUTION

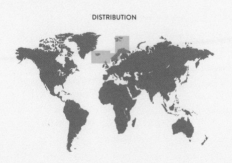

RAZORBILL

CHARADRIIFORMES

ADULT BIRD SIZE RANGE
15–17 in (38–43 cm)

ORDER ~ Charadriiformes

FAMILY ~ Alcidae

BREEDING RANGE ~ Subarctic and boreal shores on both coasts of the
Atlantic Ocean

BREEDING HABITAT ~ Coastal areas off continental-shelf waters, near
boulders and caves, or narrow cliff ledges

NEST TYPE AND PLACEMENT ~ Egg is laid on barren rock, or in shallow bowl
of rocks, shells, feathers, and vegetation

CONSERVATION STATUS ~ Least concern

Compared to other birds, Razorbills plan for the long haul in their reproductive behaviors. Individuals do not breed until four to five years of age, and the female carefully chooses her social mate by approaching different males during their courtship displays, as if to incite them to compete for her favors. Once the pair bond is established, it is maintained for life. The birds return to the same breeding colony and the same nesting site, where they display and copulate for weeks before the single egg is laid.

Once the pair reaches older age, they may skip a breeding season between nesting attempts. Taking a season off ensures the parents are in better physical condition for the next breeding attempt. As she gets older, the female may also copulate with several mates before laying her egg, to ensure that fertilization occurs. The lifespan of this species is long, with the oldest recorded individual living for 42 years.

The Razorbill is a close relative of the now-extinct Great Auk. It sports a characteristic black and white plumage, with the sexes differing only slightly in wing measurements and the different subspecies varying in beak dimensions.

DISTRIBUTION

FRATERCULA CIRRHATA

TUFTED PUFFIN

CHARADRIIFORMES

ADULT BIRD SIZE RANGE
14–15½ in (36–40 cm)

ORDER ~ Charadriiformes

FAMILY ~ Alcidae

BREEDING RANGE ~ Isolated islands in the north Pacific off North
America and Asia

BREEDING HABITAT ~ Coastal slopes, vegetation, and rocky outcroppings

NEST TYPE AND PLACEMENT ~ Simple burrow or a crevice between rocks, well lined
with plant materials and feathers

CONSERVATION STATUS ~ Least concern

The Tufted (or Crested) Puffin is a uniquely colored seabird that breeds in dense colonies on offshore locations. The single egg is incubated by both parents taking turns, and the pair also cooperate in provisioning the nestling. It takes a lot to feed the fast-growing chick, and puffin parents are often seen to return to the breeding colony with several intact fish lodged between their mandibles.

This puffin is the preferred prey species for Arctic Foxes, even when nesting in large, mixed-species breeding aggregations. To escape this predation, the puffins dig nesting burrows or select crevices that are especially hard to approach from land. The strategy also makes the species hard for researchers and conservation managers to monitor. Nesting habitat protection, including the removal of mammalian invaders on the few islands where the largest colonies are established, is a conservation priority to maintain puffin populations.

The Tufted Puffin is the largest species in its genus, easily recognized by its crest-like white-yellow head plumes in the summer. During the winter, the adults lose these distinctive feathers and become monochromatic black.

DISTRIBUTION

STRUTHIO CAMELUS

COMMON OSTRICH

STRUTHIONIFORMES

ADULT BIRD SIZE RANGE
6 ft 10 in–8 ft 10 in (2.1–2.7 m)

ORDER ~ Struthioniformes

FAMILY ~ Struthionidae

BREEDING RANGE ~ Sub-Saharan Africa, recently extinct from
the Arabian peninsula

BREEDING HABITAT ~ Desert, short grassland, savanna

NEST TYPE AND PLACEMENT ~ Simple, shallow pit in the ground

CONSERVATION STATUS ~ Least concern

The Common Ostrich is well known for the distinction between the sexes both in terms of plumage and behavior: the males' black-and-white plumes once were highly sought after by people as fashion and clothing accessories. The male incubates the eggs at night, when its plumage patterns provide for strong crypsis. In turn, the female's brown-gray plumage allows her to be camouflaged while sitting on the eggs during the day.

Nesting is a communal affair in ostriches; several females lay in the same nest. But when egg laying is complete, the dominant female culls some of the eggs by moving them out of the nest scrape, to reduce the clutch size to a manageable 20 or so eggs. These are incubated by her and a single male. The Ostrich is the largest of all living birds, and hence, when first fertilized, the egg is the largest single cell on earth.

The Common Ostrich is both large and flightless, but its wings are still used by the males for sexual displays and by both sexes during dust-bathing. The muscled legs allow them to reach high speeds.

DISTRIBUTION

CASUARIUS CASUARIUS

SOUTHERN CASSOWARY

CASUARIIFORMES

ADULT BIRD SIZE RANGE
4 ft 3 in–5 ft 7 in (1.3–1.7 m)

ORDER ~ Casuariiformes

FAMILY ~ Casuariidae

BREEDING RANGE ~ Northeastern Australia, New Guinea, and nearby
Indonesian islands

BREEDING HABITAT ~ Lowland rainforests

NEST TYPE AND PLACEMENT ~ Large ground nest built up from leaves, twigs, and
other plant materials

CONSERVATION STATUS ~ Vulnerable

The Southern Cassowary is the largest of the three extant cassowary species, and, by weight, it is the second largest living bird species, second only to the Ostrich. The female is heavier and brighter than the male, and she is also more dominant in territorial disputes between neighbors. Yet it is the father who becomes a true threat to people during the breeding season; he alone incubates the eggs and tends to the young. When threatened, he storms and uses his sharp inner toe-claws to kick up and slice through the enemy's skin and flesh.

The Southern Cassowary is conspicuously colored when viewed in a zoo or encountered at one of several camping grounds in tropical Queensland, Australia, where it has become somewhat tame. Yet, in the low light of its native dense rainforest, its black plumage, grayish casque on the top of the head, and blue-red wattle hanging below, appear more cryptic than contrasting.

The Southern Cassowary displays "reversed" sexual dimorphism in that the females are larger than males; females also have more colorful bare-skin parts and a more pronounced casque.

DISTRIBUTION

APTERYX AUSTRALIS

SOUTHERN BROWN KIWI

APTERYGIFORMES

ADULT BIRD SIZE RANGE
18–22 in (45–55 cm)

ORDER ~ Apterygiformes

FAMILY ~ Apterygidae

BREEDING RANGE ~ New Zealand

BREEDING HABITAT ~ Forest understory

NEST TYPE AND PLACEMENT ~ Underground burrows below vegetation
or between rootlets

CONSERVATION STATUS ~ Vulnerable

The female Southern Brown Kiwi invests nearly 40 percent of her body weight into laying the immense, single egg. It is no surprise that she takes several additional weeks if she lays a second egg. In turn, mostly the male is in charge of incubating the egg(s). Adult kiwis can successfully defend themselves and their eggs against stoats and rats, but the hatchlings are vulnerable until they reach about 26 oz (750 g) in weight. Therefore, when a kiwi's nesting burrow is located, conservation managers typically collect the egg, and send it to be incubated artificially at a captive hatching facility.

The Southern Brown Kiwi suffers from the same fate and population trend as all other kiwis: its numbers are dwindling as introduced mammals devastate the native flora and fauna in New Zealand. Conservation biologists predict its swift demise unless rapid nationwide protective actions are taken.

The Southern Brown Kiwi, or Tokoeka in Maori, has brownish, hair-like feathers that are neither covered in preen oil (because it has no oil gland) nor structured asymmetrically like the flight-feathers of volant birds.

DISTRIBUTION

COLINUS VIRGINIANUS

NORTHERN BOBWHITE

GALLIFORMES

ADULT BIRD SIZE RANGE
9½–11 in (24–28 cm)

ORDER ~ Galliformes

FAMILY ~ Odontophoridae

BREEDING RANGE ~ Eastern and central North America, Mexico,
the Caribbean; introduced to New Zealand

BREEDING HABITAT ~ Grasslands

NEST TYPE AND PLACEMENT ~ Simple scrape in the ground

CONSERVATION STATUS ~ Least concern, but some subspecies are endangered

The Northern Bobwhite is polyandrous, in that up to half of the females in a population mate with and lay eggs for two or more males. Both females and males incubate the nest, but a female will often abandon her first mate in search of a second, and a third, with whom she begins new clutches. This flexible and fast-paced clutch-initiation strategy may allow the species to recover after years of heavy predation, low food availability, cold weather, and intense hunting pressure, all of which are taking their toll in many regions.

The Northern Bobwhite has over 20 different subspecies. They are connected by the relative similarity of the females' plumage coloration across distant geographic areas, and separated by the different facial patterns of males. Despite their terrestrial and secretive habits, the distinctive call of the male ("bob white!") advertises the presence of this species throughout its range.

The Northern Bobwhite is a variably patterned New World quail. Its eggs are, perhaps surprisingly, immaculate white, which means that incubating adults rely on their cryptic plumage to keep the eggs safe during embryonic development.

DISTRIBUTION

TRAGOPAN CABOTI

CABOT'S TRAGOPAN

GALLIFORMES

ADULT BIRD SIZE RANGE
19½–24 in (50–61 cm)

ORDER ~ Galliformes

FAMILY ~ Phasianidae

BREEDING RANGE ~ Endemic to China

BREEDING HABITAT ~ Mature forests, with dense understory

NEST TYPE AND PLACEMENT ~ Nest is on branches of tall trees, made of leaves
and mosses, or usurping the nest of another species
off the ground

CONSERVATION STATUS ~ Vulnerable

With its colorful plumage and patches of bare orange and blue skin, there are few more spectacular sights in nature than a male Cabot's Tragopan displaying to a female. The courting male inflates the blue and red wattle (called a lappet) hanging from his throat, and erects a set of flashy black horns to frame his face, confronting the female with a fleshy explosion of color. The female carefully inspects the displaying male, and may decide to mate with him right there and then, or move on to another male's territory and watch his display.

The males demarcate their breeding territories through calling and attacking intruder males, whereas the females roam widely between territories. Only the females are in charge of the nesting, incubation, and chick protection. Inside the egg, the embryos mature fast, and the hatchlings are able to fly as soon as they emerge.

The Cabot's Tragopan is a short-tailed pheasant species
that relies on the male's colorful orange and blue
bare-skin parts to impress the female during courtship.
The female is smaller and lighter than the male.

DISTRIBUTION

PHASIANUS COLCHICUS

RING-NECKED PHEASANT

GALLIFORMES

ADULT BIRD SIZE RANGE
19½–27½ in (50–70 cm)

ORDER ~ Galliformes

FAMILY ~ Phasianidae

BREEDING RANGE ~ Asia; introduced and naturalized in many other
parts of the world including Europe, North America,
Japan, and New Zealand

BREEDING HABITAT ~ Woodlands, scrub, farms, and grasslands

NEST TYPE AND PLACEMENT ~ Ground nest concealed in grass

CONSERVATION STATUS ~ Least concern

Female Ring-necked, or Common, Pheasants choose mates based on their physical attributes, including the length of tail feathers, brightness of black ear-tufts, and, perhaps most importantly, the size of their leg spurs. These traits are thought to be related to the quality of offspring that the male would sire and this is what females are assessing. The female deposits varying amounts of steroid hormones, including testosterone, into the egg yolk, which in turn affect the sexual attractiveness and behaviors of her adult sons and daughters. The male mates with several females and the hens alone undertake all incubating and rearing duties. The chicks are independent within 12–14 days of hatching.

The Ring-necked Pheasant is historically one of the earliest introduced and naturalized species in Europe, having established itself from released stock over hundreds of years, so that in many places it is treated as a native species.

The Ring-necked Pheasant is a long-tailed and sexually dimorphic species; the different subspecies vary in the patterning of their males' face and neck, whereas both females and chicks are cryptic in feather coloration.

DISTRIBUTION

PAVO MUTICUS

GREEN PEAFOWL

GALLIFORMES

ADULT BIRD SIZE RANGE
3 ft 3 in–7 ft 4 in (100–224 cm)

ORDER ~ Galliformes

FAMILY ~ Phasianidae

BREEDING RANGE ~ Remnant populations throughout Southeast Asia

BREEDING HABITAT ~ Tropical dry and seasonal forests

NEST TYPE AND PLACEMENT ~ Scrape nest on the ground

CONSERVATION STATUS ~ Endangered

The Green Peafowl looks familiar, as it resembles the Indian Peafowl (or peacock) in its coloration and the male's decorated train. But there are notable differences. For instance, the species' bright green and blue plumage coloration is shared by both the male and the female, making it sexually monochromatic. The male weighs three to four times as much as the female, which marks it out as one of the most size-dimorphic of modern bird species.

The mating behavior of the Green Peafowl is also distinctive. Instead of forming leks, like Indian Peacocks do, the Green Peafowl maintains distinct male territories, and strong affiliations with one or more females in that territory. The parents continue their association after the eggs hatch, and so entire family groups of parents and growing chicks can be seen roosting together at night, in trees, for safety from ground predators.

The Green Peafowl is distinct both because the females and males have similarly bright and iridescent coloration and because the upper-tail covers (not the actual tails) of both sexes overlap the short and stubby tail-feathers.

DISTRIBUTION

NEOPHRON PERCNOPTERUS

EGYPTIAN VULTURE

ACCIPITRIFORMES

ADULT BIRD SIZE RANGE
18½–27½ in (47–70 cm)

ORDER ~ Accipitriformes

FAMILY ~ Accipitridae

BREEDING RANGE ~ Southwestern Europe, northern and equatorial
Africa, the Middle East, and south Asia

BREEDING HABITAT ~ Dry plains and lowland forests; often near human
settlements, including large cities

NEST TYPE AND PLACEMENT ~ Cliffs or buildings, made of sticks, leaves,
and garbage

CONSERVATION STATUS ~ Endangered; despite the large distribution, local
populations have suffered 30–75 percent declines
in recent decades

82

Egyptian vultures are typically seen alone or in pairs during the day, but aggregate in groups at night for roosting in trees or on building roofs. Breeding takes place in a haphazardly constructed stick nest, or in a previously used but refurbished eagle's nest. Occasionally, females mate with two males, both of whom may attend and help raise the young in a single nest. With far fewer freely available mammalian carrion, due to declining large wildlife stocks as well as modern practices of swiftly removing carcasses, these vultures have suffered severe population losses.

The Egyptian Vulture is one of the most resourceful species of birds, making innovative use of diverse materials available to them in nature, and especially around human settlements. For example, birds have been seen holding sticks in their beaks to rake up wool left behind from sheep shearing. They then carry the wool to their nests where it provides a soft lining.

The Egyptian Vulture is a variably colored bird of prey, with juveniles accumulating grayer and whiter feathers as they mature. Its bright-yellow-skinned face allows it to forage deep inside carcasses without spoiling its plumage.

DISTRIBUTION

AQUILA CHRYSAETOS

GOLDEN EAGLE

ACCIPITRIFORMES

ADULT BIRD SIZE RANGE
27½–33 in (70–84 cm)

ORDER ~ Accipitriformes

FAMILY ~ Accipitridae

BREEDING RANGE ~ Temperate and subarctic North America, Eurasia,
and North Africa

BREEDING HABITAT ~ Grasslands, tundra, and other mostly open habitats

NEST TYPE AND PLACEMENT ~ Large and bulky stick nest lined with leaves and
mosses, placed in trees and on cliffs, occasionally
on human structures

CONSERVATION STATUS ~ Least concern

Golden Eagles form a long-lasting pair bond and cooperation is essential for successful breeding. Mates maintain a vast and exclusive all-purpose territory: they both breed and forage on it, and they attack intruding eagles to keep the prey-base to themselves. The nests are vast structures, with the pair returning and reusing the previous year's nest, while continually building and expanding it year after year. These huge raptors have few predators, so there is no selective pressure to hide the nest and eggs.

The Golden Eagle is one of the largest birds of prey, occurring throughout the northern hemisphere where it feeds on larger ground-dwelling mammals and birds or seeks out carrion to consume. Occasionally, mated pairs hunt cooperatively, with one bird distracting the fleeing prey while the second bird approaches to catch it from the other side.

The Golden Eagle is broadly distributed, with its name originating from the golden hues of its neck and nape feathers. Juveniles display several patches of white but they lose these spots as they mature.

DISTRIBUTION

PEREGRINE FALCON

FALCONIFORMES

ADULT BIRD SIZE RANGE
16–20 in (41–51 cm)

ORDER ~ Falconiformes

FAMILY ~ Falconidae

BREEDING RANGE ~ Worldwide; found on all continents except
Antarctica

BREEDING HABITAT ~ A broad range of habitats; generally needs cliffs or
tall buildings for nesting and open areas for hunting
and provisioning

NEST TYPE AND PLACEMENT ~ A shallow scrape, with no lining materials added.
Placed on a cliff or building ledge

CONSERVATION STATUS ~ Least concern

In the early 1960s, Peregrine Falcons declined catastrophically in North America and Europe. Comparing eggs from failed nests with those from museum collections, researchers found thinning of shells through time. The cause was traced to DDT, a long-lasting pesticide that moves up the food chain, concentrating in top predators such as raptorial birds. In the female's reproductive tract, DDT byproducts prevented calcium from being supplied to the shell; such frail eggs broke during incubation.

Peregrines became endangered in the United States, but a DDT ban, plus intensive breeding and reintroduction efforts, resulted in a strong recovery and, ultimately, their removal from the endangered species list. A key factor was the Peregrine's ability to become urbanized and adapt to nesting on tall buildings. Peregrine Falcons are fast fliers, able to accelerate to 120 mph (200 km/h) during steep hunting dives for their avian prey, including city pigeons.

The Peregrine Falcon is distributed globally, occurring on six continents. Its pointed wings, longish tail, and bullet-shaped body form adaptations to make it the fastest flying bird in pursuit of its also volant prey.

DISTRIBUTION

TETRAX TETRAX

LITTLE BUSTARD

OTIDIFORMES

ADULT BIRD SIZE RANGE
16½–17½ in (42–45 cm)

ORDER ~ Otidiformes

FAMILY ~ Otididae

BREEDING RANGE ~ Europe, northwestern Africa, western and central Asia

BREEDING HABITAT ~ Dry grasslands, low-intensity agricultural fields

NEST TYPE AND PLACEMENT ~ Shallow depression in the ground, under grassy cover

CONSERVATION STATUS ~ Near threatened

Little Bustards are habitat specialists, occurring in open grassland. Their populations are threatened throughout much of their range because of the expansion of agricultural fields. Living in open country is critical for these birds, because courtship behaviors rely mostly on visual signals given by the males, displaying in loose aggregations, to attract the females. Once mated, the female receives no further help from the male, and undertakes all nesting and parental duties on her own.

Male Little Bustards invest most of their time in the spring selecting and protecting their display sites. Older males tend to dominate younger males in confrontations that allow them to settle on more central patches. Interested females tend to visit and mate with older and more dominant males. This type of mating system, where males concentrate in an area to display competitively for females, is called lekking. It is seen in many other avian lineages, including Galliformes.

The Little Bustard is a large terrestrial bird, despite being one of the smallest bustards. Its prominent black and white patterned front serves in the males' long-distance visual displays to interested females arriving to the lek.

DISTRIBUTION

BUBO VIRGINIANUS

GREAT HORNED OWL

STRIGIFORMES

FEMALE

MALE

ADULT BIRD SIZE RANGE
18–25 in (46–63 cm)

ORDER ~ Strigiformes

FAMILY ~ Strigidae

BREEDING RANGE ~ North, Central, and South America

BREEDING HABITAT ~ Forests and parklands, wooded areas near
agricultural fields

NEST TYPE AND PLACEMENT ~ Natural cavities, burrows, or tree holes excavated by
other animals, abandoned squirrel nests; no lining

CONSERVATION STATUS ~ Least concern

Male Great Horned Owls call throughout the year, uttering their characteristic deep hoots, while females only call during the mating season. Once vocal contact is established, the potential mates move closer to one another and display a series of bobs and bows as they continue their mutual assessment. When food is abundant, the male provisions the female during incubation and the early stages of chick rearing, whereas in years of food scarcity, the female leaves the nest soon after the eggs hatch to help catch food for the nestlings.

The Great Horned Owl, also known as the Tiger Owl, is a widespread, well-known, and powerful nocturnal predator; it commonly takes large prey, including skunks and rabbits. Nighttime predation on nestlings was also a weighty hindrance in the reintroduction efforts of the Peregrine Falcon in some regions.

The Great Horned Owl is a large nocturnal predator, with mottled brown and beige feathers. It is typically lighter below, which may help it to approach its prey undetected during its hunts on more moon-lit nights.

DISTRIBUTION

BUBO SCANDIACUS

SNOWY OWL

STRIGIFORMES

ADULT BIRD SIZE RANGE
20½–28 in (52–71 cm)

ORDER ~ Strigiformes

FAMILY ~ Strigidae

BREEDING RANGE ~ Arctic Eurasia and North America

BREEDING HABITAT ~ Tundra, and open coastal dunes

NEST TYPE AND PLACEMENT ~ Shallow hollow, scraped in the ground

CONSERVATION STATUS ~ Least concern

The Snowy Owl is superbly adapted to life in a landscape where predator and prey can both see far away: it is a tall predator whose white plumage makes it less conspicuous during the constant Arctic daylight. It uses small mounds in the open tundra for nesting and for surveying the landscape to sight potential danger and suitable prey. Flying low above the landscape, this owl searches for small rodents and birds, and consumes its prey by swallowing it whole.

The female incubates the eggs while the male stands guard nearby; both sexes vigorously attack any predators that approach the nest. However, although this species is one of the largest predators in the tundra, its nest is still vulnerable to attacks by Great Skuas, eagles, and Arctic Foxes. Nonetheless, because of the aggressive defense of their clutch, other birds, including Snow Geese, are often found nesting near Snowy Owls. The safety of these birds' eggs is increased by their proximity to the Snowy Owls' nest sites.

The Snowy Owl is, according to recent DNA tests, a close relative of the horned owls in the same genus. Its uniquely white plumage and bright yellow eyes, however, provide it with an unmistakable appearance.

DISTRIBUTION

ZENAIDA MACROURA

MOURNING DOVE

COLUMBIFORMES

ADULT BIRD SIZE RANGE
9–13½ in (23–34 cm)

ORDER ~ Columbiformes

FAMILY ~ Columbidae

BREEDING RANGE ~ Temperate North America

BREEDING HABITAT ~ Open woodlands, also scrub and semi-deserts,
city parks

NEST TYPE AND PLACEMENT ~ Twig, pine needle, and grass platform, no lining;
placed on tree branches, but also on the ground
or on building ledges

CONSERVATION STATUS ~ Least concern

The Mourning Dove is a common, widespread, and adaptable bird; it can successfully reproduce in urban areas, open forests, and the deserts of the American West. In arid regions, the adults are able to drink slightly saline spring water, without getting dehydrated. These mid-sized doves consume seeds all day long, ingesting and digesting 20 to 30 percent of their body weight on a daily basis.

The mating season begins with conspicuous flights and chases by both members of the eventual pair. The male collects most of the nesting materials, which are then woven together, albeit loosely, by the female; the nest is so loose that the eggs are sometimes visible from underneath. The two eggs are bright white, but they are never uncovered because the two sexes take turns to incubate them. Instead of regurgitating seeds, both parents provision the young with nutritious and energy-rich "crop-milk," a secretion from the bird's neck pouch.

The Mourning Dove is subtly colored by hues of brown and pink, with distinctive black markings around its body. Its appearance, however, is effectively cryptic, as the dove parent sits on its clutch during incubation.

DISTRIBUTION

COMMON CUCKOO

CUCULIFORMES

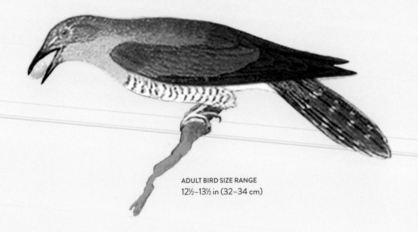

ADULT BIRD SIZE RANGE
12½–13½ in (32–34 cm)

ORDER ~ Cuculiformes

FAMILY ~ Cuculidae

BREEDING RANGE ~ Temperate Eurasia

BREEDING HABITAT ~ Forests, open woodlands, reed beds

NEST TYPE AND PLACEMENT ~ Obligate brood parasite, lays eggs in other species' nests

CONSERVATION STATUS ~ Least concern

This species is the world's best-studied obligate brood parasitic bird: the female cuckoo seeks out suitable and active nests of small songbirds in which to lay her eggs, to be cared for by the unwitting host. Host females typically lay some of their eggs in the early morning, and then leave the nest to feed themselves in order to nourish the next morning's egg. Capitalizing on their absence, the cuckoo female lays her egg in the mid-afternoon, thus avoiding detection by the soon-to-be foster-parents of the cuckoo chick. Once the cuckoo chick hatches, it quickly evicts all other eggs.

To reduce the chances of detection by the host, cuckoos have evolved egg-color specific races, called gentes: females of the same gens lay eggs that mimic the color and maculation patterns of the egg of a host species. Similarities in light reflectance between the cuckoo and the host eggshells lower the rate of rejection of the parasitic egg by the nest owners.

The Common Cuckoo is a polychromatic species: whereas all males are grayish, with a prominent hawk-like barred chest and bright yellow eyes, the females can be either grayish (common) or rusty-red (rare) in appearance.

DISTRIBUTION

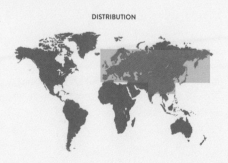

CALYPTE COSTAE

COSTA'S HUMMINGBIRD

APODIFORMES

ADULT BIRD SIZE RANGE
3½–4 in (9–10 cm)

ORDER ~ Apodiformes

FAMILY ~ Trochilidae

BREEDING RANGE ~ Southwestern North America

BREEDING HABITAT ~ Desert and semi-desert; chaparral

NEST TYPE AND PLACEMENT ~ Cup nest on branches of shrubs and trees,
composed of vegetation and spider silk

CONSERVATION STATUS ~ Least concern

This hummingbird is an inhabitant of the dry Sonoran desert in the southwestern United States. Some populations are migratory into coastal Mexico, but others stay in place year-round. If an adult experiences a severely cold night in the desert, it may go into torpor by dropping its heart rate from 500 to 50 beats per minute, thus saving critical energy for its next morning's activity.

Males engage in aerial displays and battle for breeding grounds for one to three weeks before the females arrive. When they do arrive, the males compete with neighboring males for the attention of mates. Once sperm-transfer is complete, however, the female is in full charge of breeding, from nesting to fledging. She builds a nest by constructing a loosely knit cup of plant matter and spider silk on a branch, which she then finishes to form a cup shape by running her chin along the rim of the nest while sitting inside it.

The Costa's Hummingbird is small and colorful, with males sporting an iridescent purple crown and gorget (throat patch), that become the brightest when viewed head-on as the male displays to attract females for mating.

DISTRIBUTION

ALCEDO ATTHIS

COMMON KINGFISHER

CORACIIFORMES

ADULT BIRD SIZE RANGE
6½–6¾ in (16–17 cm)

ORDER ~ Coraciiformes

FAMILY ~ Alcedinidae

BREEDING RANGE ~ Temperate and southern Eurasia

BREEDING HABITAT ~ Lake and river shores with dense vegetation

NEST TYPE AND PLACEMENT ~ Cavity nest, dug into river bank or quarry wall

CONSERVATION STATUS ~ Least concern

This kingfisher is territorial; the members of a pair will defend their own adjacent territories much of the time, but combine feeding territories in the early spring when nesting begins. Nest building, incubation, and chick raising are shared by the two mates; the female takes most of the night shifts, while the male changes guard with her during the day. As the chicks grow, they approach the cavity entrance to feed, leaving the rest of the nesting tunnel and chamber foul smelling with fecal matter, remains of uneaten prey, and regurgitated food pellets.

This is a strictly aquatic feeder, and so the presence of the Common Kingfisher is often taken as an indicator of high-quality, clear waters in a habitat. This is because the species requires a transparent water column to locate and catch fish by plunge diving after hovering in the air or sallying from a prominent perching site.

The Common Kingfisher is one of the most colorful European bird species, sporting a bright blue back and crown and a rusty-orange throat and belly. The sexes are identical in plumage, but differ in beak colors (the female is shown here).

DISTRIBUTION

MEROPS PERSICUS

BLUE-CHEEKED BEE-EATER

CORACIIFORMES

ADULT BIRD SIZE RANGE
6½–15½ in (17–40 cm)

ORDER ~ Coraciiformes

FAMILY ~ Meropidae

BREEDING RANGE ~ Northern Africa, western Asia

BREEDING HABITAT ~ Dry savanna, semi-deserts

NEST TYPE AND PLACEMENT ~ Burrow nest, excavated in a river bank

CONSERVATION STATUS ~ Least concern

The breeding grounds of the Blue-cheeked Bee-Eater are in arid open areas punctuated by distant tree stands, with most pairs dispersed into lone nesting sites, or small loose colonies occasionally near other, more sociable bee-eaters. In the non-breeding season, the species forms large flocks that migrate to sub-Saharan Africa where they can often be found in open, grassy fields, along large rivers and in coastal mangroves on both the east and west coasts of the continent.

The two parents together excavate the nest tunnel and they also share feeding the young equitably and without the assistance of adult helpers. Like all bee-eaters, the adults frequently feed nestlings bees and wasps; they catch the insects in their long sharp bills and bang them against a tree branch or some other substrate to remove the stingers before the chicks eat them.

The Blue-cheeked Bee-Eater is a slim-bodied and narrow-billed aerial insectivore, with a green plumage, a blue face, a black eye-line, and an orange throat. The sexes share feather coloration but the females' tail-streamers are shorter.

DISTRIBUTION

RAMPHASTOS TUCANUS

WHITE-THROATED TOUCAN

PICIFORMES

ADULT BIRD SIZE RANGE
21–24 in (53–61 cm)

ORDER ~ Piciformes

FAMILY ~ Ramphastidae

BREEDING RANGE ~ Tropical South America

BREEDING HABITAT ~ Humid forests, riverine woodlands, palm groves

NEST TYPE AND PLACEMENT ~ Unlined cavity nest; in rotting tree or in abandoned woodpecker cavity

CONSERVATION STATUS ~ Least concern

The White-throated Toucan is a conspicuous and colorful neotropical bird. It feeds on ripe fruit and berries, but also consumes fleshy insects, lizards, and chicks out of the nests of other birds when the opportunities arise. The two sexes are similar in appearance, with the male somewhat larger than the female. The sex roles, however, are equitable, with the mates spending much of the day foraging together. They also select the nesting cavity, incubate the eggs, and feed the chicks together, or by taking turns.

Nestlings of this toucan species have a thick layer of skin on the heel to protect them from the rough structure of the barren tree cavity floor. The hatchlings are naked and blind, and rely on their parents for brooding and feeding in the nest. Even when the fledglings leave the nest, they need several weeks to become fully independent, and they take flight for short, undulating stretches between tall fruit-bearing trees.

The White-throated Toucan is a large and colorful tropical frugivore; its beak-color variant subspecies were once thought to form three separate species, but behavioral data shows that they freely interbreed whenever their ranges overlap.

DISTRIBUTION

WILLIAMSON'S SAPSUCKER

PICIFORMES

MALE

FEMALE

ADULT BIRD SIZE RANGE
8–9 in (20–23 cm)

ORDER ~ Piciformes

FAMILY ~ Picidae

BREEDING RANGE ~ Western North America

BREEDING HABITAT ~ Coniferous and mixed montane forests

NEST TYPE AND PLACEMENT ~ Cavity nest, excavated anew in conifer stands

CONSERVATION STATUS ~ Least concern

Most black-and-white plumaged woodpeckers show slight sexual dichromatism, with the male having a little more red coloration around his head. But the sexes of this sapsucker are so dramatically different that early naturalists originally thought they were separate species; the male is predominantly black, white, and yellow while the female is more cryptically striped with earth tones. Pair bonds are based on a single female–male coalition and both parents provide parental duties.

For nesting, this sapsucker requires trees with cores that are softened by fungal infections; such a soft core facilitates nest excavation, which occurs anew each year. Old cavities are not reused. To feed the young, this species adds ants to its predominantly sap- and phloem-based diet to provide a better source of protein for the developing nestlings.

The Williamson's Sapsucker is a dichromatic species, whose female was originally described as the black-breasted woodpecker. The males' black plumage is dotted by prominent white patterns, a yellow belly, and a small red throat patch.

DISTRIBUTION

DRYOCOPUS PILEATUS

PILEATED WOODPECKER

PICIFORMES

ADULT BIRD SIZE RANGE
15½–19½ in (40–49 cm)

ORDER ~ Piciformes

FAMILY ~ Picidae

BREEDING RANGE ~ Temperate North America

BREEDING HABITAT ~ Deciduous and coniferous forests, wooded parks

NEST TYPE AND PLACEMENT ~ Large cavity, carved into dead trees and logs;
unlined except for woodchips

CONSERVATION STATUS ~ Least concern

This is the largest North American woodpecker, accepting that both the Ivory-billed and the Imperial Woodpecker are now extinct. It maintains its pair bond throughout the year, with the mates occupying a year-round feeding and nesting territory. It prefers to live in mature wood lots, but will inhabit smaller and younger stands, as long as several large trees are still standing for feeding and nesting. The male selects and begins to carve out the nesting chamber, and the female contributes if she accepts the location.

Once a nesting chamber is complete, the female begins laying her eggs on a daily basis. She spends many of the daylight hours in the nest during the laying period, while the male roosts in that cavity at night. During the incubation period, the pair is very quiet and secretive and the eggs are covered by one of the adults 99 percent of the time, with the male solely taking charge of nocturnal shifts.

The Pileated Woodpecker is a still common, large species of the North American forests. It forms part of a broadly ranging, black-white-and-red colored genus of woodpeckers, whose species occur in South America and Eurasia, too.

DISTRIBUTION

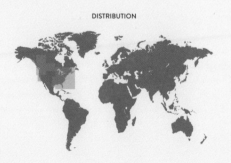

CONTOPUS COOPERI

OLIVE-SIDED FLYCATCHER

PASSERIFORMES

ADULT BIRD SIZE RANGE
7–8 in (18–20 cm)

ORDER ~ Passeriformes

FAMILY ~ Tyrannidae

BREEDING RANGE ~ North America

BREEDING HABITAT ~ Mid- to high-elevation and coniferous forests, often
near clearings and other edges

NEST TYPE AND PLACEMENT ~ Open cup of twigs, roots, and lichens, placed along
a thin branch of a pine or spruce, in a fork or on top
of a cluster of fallen needles

CONSERVATION STATUS ~ Near threatened

This flycatcher really lives up to its name by hunting and capturing flying prey in the air after spotting it from an exposed perch in the forest or forest edge. Breeding pairs maintain a large exclusive area around the nest and defend it aggressively. Population numbers for this species have been steadily declining by 3 percent or more yearly over the past decade, resulting in its "near threatened" status.

This flycatcher is a long-distance migrant, which complicates conservation efforts. It arrives on its breeding grounds very late in the spring, so it has limited time to establish the pair bond, initiate the nest, and fledge the young. Even so, if the first or second nesting attempt fails, the pair remains together and initiates a new nest at a new site, often repeatedly. But later breeding attempts fail more frequently than earlier attempts because as summer turns into fall, there is little time to complete a full breeding cycle.

The Olive-sided Flycatcher is a drab and small tyrant flycatcher. It feeds and displays during courtship on the wing, with both sexes catching insects in mid-air and the male singing in flight to attract females.

DISTRIBUTION

MYIARCHUS CINERASCENS

ASH-THROATED FLYCATCHER

PASSERIFORMES

ADULT BIRD SIZE RANGE
7½–8½ in (19–21 cm)

ORDER ~ Passeriformes

FAMILY ~ Tyrannidae

BREEDING RANGE ~ Western North America, including northern
Mexico

BREEDING HABITAT ~ Desert scrub, deciduous and mixed forests,
riparian corridors

NEST TYPE AND PLACEMENT ~ Nests in cavities, including a broad range of natural
or artificial holes. Inside, the nest cup is made of dry
grass, stems, manure, and leaves; lined with hair,
feathers, and plant fibers

CONSERVATION STATUS ~ Least concern

Though this species looks and acts like a flycatcher, sallying from perch to perch and observing its surroundings for potential prey and danger, it catches most of its prey by gleaning insects off foliage and branches, rather than taking them in midair. It is very similar in plumage coloration and stature to other flycatchers in the same genus, but the different species can be told apart by their distinctive vocalizations. As with all suboscine birds, the chicks do not learn their calls, but inherit them from their parents.

Across most of its range, this species is migratory, which places a definite time constraint on its breeding schedule: farther north, there is only time for a single breeding attempt per summer. Even more restrictive is the availability of natural cavities for nesting. Many hole-breeding species are resident or local migrants, giving them a head-start to claiming a cavity over these late-arriving, long-distance migrant flycatchers.

The Ash-throated Flycatcher is nearly identical in its appearance to other species in the same genus, but its vocal repertoire is uniquely species-specific. In turn, the sexes are identical in both size and plumage coloration.

DISTRIBUTION

TYRANNUS TYRANNUS

EASTERN KINGBIRD

PASSERIFORMES

ADULT BIRD SIZE RANGE
8–9 in (20–23 cm)

ORDER ~ Passeriformes

FAMILY ~ Tyrannidae

BREEDING RANGE ~ Eastern and central North America

BREEDING HABITAT ~ Fields scattered with trees, orchards, forest edges

NEST TYPE AND PLACEMENT ~ Open cup nest, made of wiry twigs and glasses,
placed in a shrub, tree, or on top of a stump or a pole

CONSERVATION STATUS ~ Least concern

This species is a long-distance migrant, moving between temperate North America and Amazonian South America. Once the birds return to their breeding site, the male typically settles and begins to defend his territory, often the same general area as the year before. If the female is his mate from the prior year, the breeding can begin a week after arrival; otherwise it takes two to three weeks for a new pair to start nesting. The nest is often rebuilt in the same spot as the previous year. If a nest is lost or damaged due to the weather, the female quickly builds another nest for another clutch of eggs.

This kingbird is well known for its aggressive territorial defense, which includes protecting the often conspicuously placed nest from larger potential predators, including jays, hawks, and squirrels. Clearly, camouflage for the nest is not required when it is under the protection of a true "tyrant" flycatcher, as implied by the Latin genus name *Tyrannus* for this species and its close relatives.

The Eastern Kingbird is a medium-bodied, large-headed flycatcher. The sexes appear similar in size and coloration, but maintain distinctly different postures when perching: the males typically sit upright and have a semi-permanent crest.

DISTRIBUTION

LANIUS LUDOVICIANUS

LOGGERHEAD SHRIKE

PASSERIFORMES

ADULT BIRD SIZE RANGE
8–9 in (20–23 cm)

ORDER ~ Passeriformes

FAMILY ~ Laniidae

BREEDING RANGE ~ Temperate and tropical North America

BREEDING HABITAT ~ Open fields, orchards, pastures with sparse bushes
and trees

NEST TYPE AND PLACEMENT ~ Cup nest in tree, constructed of twigs, lined with
fine grasses, feathers, hair, and other filaments

CONSERVATION STATUS ~ Near threatened

This shrike is the only endemic North American species in a large genus and family that is distributed mostly in the Old World. Despite its small stature, it surveys the habitat from a high vantage point and uses its thick, hooked bill to capture and crush prey, from arthropods to lizards and mice.

Breeding begins early in the spring, and in southern regions, where this species is resident all year long. Pairs may stay together through the winter, and come into reproductive condition synchronously and more quickly than newly formed pairs. Nesting materials are gathered by both sexes, but the female constructs the nest with little help. She is also in charge of incubating the eggs and brooding the chicks, while the male feeds her at the nest and provides food for the young family during the first days after hatching. Later, both sexes feed the growing young and defend the nest.

The Loggerhead Shrike is one of only two shrike species native to the Americas, along with the Northern Shrike. Both species are white, gray, and black, but Loggerheads are smaller, more slender, and feature a less sharply hooked bill.

DISTRIBUTION

YELLOW-THROATED VIREO

PASSERIFORMES

ADULT BIRD SIZE RANGE
5–6 in (13–15 cm)

ORDER ~ Passeriformes

FAMILY ~ Vireonidae

BREEDING RANGE ~ Eastern and central North America

BREEDING HABITAT ~ Edge habitats of mature deciduous and mixed
forests, including woodlands bordering rivers,
swamps, roads, and parks

NEST TYPE AND PLACEMENT ~ Open, suspended cup in a tree, with its rim attached
to a horizontal fork of a small branch

CONSERVATION STATUS ~ Least concern

This vireo used to inhabit large urban parks, including in New York City and Boston, but disappeared from most of these sites due to the intensive spraying of insecticides. Yet the overall population of this naturally uncommon species has been steadily increasing over the last few decades in rural regions, perhaps associated with the maturation of many previously clear-cut Eastern deciduous forests, whose edges provide its most suitable breeding habitat.

The males return from migration just days before the females do, and potential mates assess each other during courtship displays, which include the male leading the female to several feasible nesting sites. Once the mates have settled, the male starts building the nest at one of these sites; the female soon takes over construction duties and she alone completes the nest. The female also spends more time incubating the eggs, as she sits on them all night, and changes guard with the male only during daytime.

The Yellow-throated Vireo is brightly colored, yet its olive, yellow, and white feathers, shared between the sexes and between adults and juveniles, blend in well against the greenish light of the forest canopy, making this species hard to spot.

DISTRIBUTION

INDIAN PARADISE FLYCATCHER

PASSERIFORMES

ADULT BIRD SIZE RANGE
7½–8 in (19–20 cm)
plus 12 in (30 cm) tail

ORDER – Passeriformes

FAMILY – Monarchidae

BREEDING RANGE – Central and south Asia

BREEDING HABITAT – Dense and mature tropical forests

NEST TYPE AND PLACEMENT – Tightly constructed cup nest, made
with twigs, leaves, and spider webs

CONSERVATION STATUS – Least concern

This flycatcher, along with several of its relatives, is perhaps best known not for its elongated and elaborate tail plumes, but for the male's plumage polymorphism which includes long-tailed white males, long-tailed rufous males, and short-tailed rufous males. All three of these male morphs can be sexually mature, and attempt to attract females to breed in socially monogamous pairs. Those females who mate with long-tailed males begin to nest earlier in the season and lay more eggs than females mated with short-tailed males. However, researchers have found no apparent difference in reproductive success between the white and rufous long-tailed males.

Once the eggs hatch, the chicks solicit parental care by begging loudly and opening their bright yellow gape whenever an adult lands on the nest's rim. Nourished by both parents, who deliver insects, these chicks grow quickly, and are able to leave and flutter out of the nest on their own wings just 10 to 11 days after hatching.

The Indian Paradise Flycatcher is a recently recognized species, one of three from the former Asian Paradise Flycatcher. Its male-specific polymorphism includes two color (rusty and white) and tail (shorter in young birds) morphs.

DISTRIBUTION

CYANOCITTA CRISTATA

BLUE JAY

PASSERIFORMES

ADULT BIRD SIZE RANGE
10–12 in (25–30 cm)

ORDER ~ Passeriformes

FAMILY ~ Corvidae

BREEDING RANGE ~ Eastern and central North America

BREEDING HABITAT ~ Deciduous and coniferous forests, parks, suburban
developments, and wooded urban areas

NEST TYPE AND PLACEMENT ~ Open cup, made of twigs, sticks, and mud, lined
with grass and rootlets; placed in trees

CONSERVATION STATUS ~ Least concern

The Blue Jay is a common, bright, and loud inhabitant of forests and wood lots as well as cities, towns, and farms throughout its range. Many people can count this endemic North American species in their personal list of familiar birds, in addition to introduced sparrows, starlings, and pigeons. The Blue Jay occurs even in the most densely settled urban areas, as long as there are a few trees on the quieter side streets, where they can build their nests in the high canopy.

Only the female incubates the eggs and she also broods the young chicks, while the male provides her and the whole young family with all the food they need during the first few days after hatching. To keep the nest clean and hygienic, Blue Jay parents consume broken eggshells soon after hatching and swallow the fecal sacs produced by the chicks after each feeding bout. This also serves to eliminate any visual and olfactory cues that predators might use to find the nest.

The Blue Jay is the most conspicuous of corvids in Eastern and Central North America, named after its erect crest displayed during social and anti-predatory interactions. The sexes are similar in their blue, white, and black coloration.

DISTRIBUTION

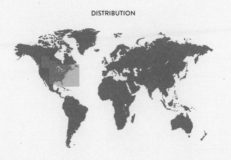

CORVUS CORAX

COMMON RAVEN

PASSERIFORMES

ADULT BIRD SIZE RANGE
22–27 in (56–69 cm)

ORDER ~ Passeriformes

FAMILY ~ Corvidae

BREEDING RANGE ~ Temperate and Arctic northern hemisphere,
including montane subtropical regions

BREEDING HABITAT ~ Forested areas, with open fields or coastal
areas nearby

NEST TYPE AND PLACEMENT ~ Large platform of sticks, branches, and twigs, lined
with mud, grasses, lichens, and plant and animal
fibers; on cliff ledges, in trees, and on power lines

CONSERVATION STATUS ~ Least concern

The Common Raven is one of the most widespread perching birds in the world. Ravens are well known for their high intelligence, including the ability to solve problems that require insight and foresight. Their mental powers include detailed long-term memory, along with fine-tuned vocal signaling that allows for sophisticated communication between individuals.

Ravens mate for life, but unpaired males occasionally visit a female when her mate is out of sight. Once the pair bond is formed, and a breeding territory is established, nest building can begin. The male assists with providing the larger sticks and branches for the platform of the nest, and then the female completes the nest and lines the inner cup with soft wool and hair for the eggs. Few of the nests survive in usable condition for the next year, but many pairs still re-nest or repair what little is left at the previous year's location.

The Common Raven is a uniformly black bird, and may possibly weigh in as the heaviest of songbirds. The morphological uniformity of the species does not parallel its complex evolutionary history as revealed by DNA.

DISTRIBUTION

BEARDED REEDLING

PASSERIFORMES

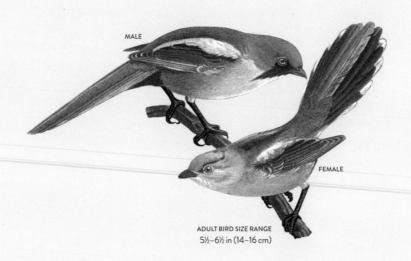

MALE

FEMALE

ADULT BIRD SIZE RANGE
5½–6½ in (14–16 cm)

ORDER ~ Passeriformes

FAMILY ~ Panuridae

BREEDING RANGE ~ Temperate Europe and Asia

BREEDING HABITAT ~ Wetlands with extensive reed beds

NEST TYPE AND PLACEMENT ~ Cup nest woven around reed stems with cobwebs,
made of grass and strips of reed leaves, and lined
with plant and animal fibers

CONSERVATION STATUS ~ Least concern

This species is a specialist inhabitant of large, freshwater reed beds; blending in to the background of reed stems and flowers, it uses its long tail and flexible feet to balance. It preys on aphids during the summer, and alters its digestive physiology to feed on reed seeds during the winter, as it remains a resident in its home marsh or swamp year-round. In fact, juveniles often disperse just outside the immediate vicinity of their natal territory, and DNA fingerprinting has revealed that inbreeding in some of these small, closed populations occurs quite frequently.

This species adopts two different tactics for breeding. Pairs may settle on their own, or nest as part of a loose colony. Females are larger and in better condition when breeding in groups, and more often engage in extra-pair matings; they are less faithful to the pair bond when neighboring males have longer beard and tail plumes relative to their own social partner.

The Bearded Reedling is a morphologically and genetically unique songbird, with no other species in its genus and family. The males have a prominent black moustache whereas the females lack this trait.

DISTRIBUTION

PETROCHELIDON PYRRHONOTA

CLIFF SWALLOW

PASSERIFORMES

ADULT BIRD SIZE RANGE
5–6 in (13–15 cm)

ORDER ~ Passeriformes

FAMILY ~ Hirundinidae

BREEDING RANGE ~ Temperate and boreal North America

BREEDING HABITAT ~ Open canyons, foothills, open areas near water

NEST TYPE AND PLACEMENT ~ Covered bowl, with a side entrance tunnel, attached to cliffs, bridge overhangs, culverts, and other artificial structures; made of mud pellets, lined with grass

CONSERVATION STATUS ~ Least concern

Cliff Swallows are known for their colonial breeding, both because of the sheer number of their mud nests pasted against each other underneath midwestern highway overpasses, and because the most important decision prior to mating in this species is to gauge the distribution and suitability of different-sized colonies in the spring. Early experience matters critically for these birds: those individuals that were hatched in small or large colonies tend to prefer to settle in small or large colonies, respectively.

Once the colony site is chosen, the males quickly claim ownership of an old nest, or start building a new nest, even if they have not yet been chosen by a female. The females tend to spend a few days prospecting between suitable colonies, then quickly settle and find a mate. Both sexes help to complete the nest, incubate the eggs, and feed the young.

The Cliff Swallow is best recognized from its prominent rump patch and the triangular white forehead spot, surrounded by rusty-black head feathers. Facial markings vary between subspecies and different age classes but not between the sexes.

DISTRIBUTION

SITTA PUSILLA

BROWN-HEADED NUTHATCH

PASSERIFORMES

ADULT BIRD SIZE RANGE
4–4½ in (10–11 cm)

ORDER ~ Passeriformes

FAMILY ~ Sittidae

BREEDING RANGE ~ Southeastern North America

BREEDING HABITAT ~ Native mature, and cultivated, southern pine forests

NEST TYPE AND PLACEMENT ~ Cavity nest, typically newly excavated, but sometimes reusing old woodpecker holes or adopting nestboxes

CONSERVATION STATUS ~ Least concern

On breeding territories the Brown-headed Nuthatch has a social structure which is based around a monogamous pair bond, assisted at many nests by one to three helpers. These helpers can be younger but sexually mature males who forgo direct breeding, and probably assist their father, older brother, or some other relative across the reproductive cycle. They contribute toward excavating the nest, lining the nest hole, feeding the chicks, removing excrement, and defending the territory. Nests with at least one helper have more than 50 percent greater breeding success than nests without any.

This small nuthatch species occurs today only in the southeastern United States, and its strong preference to breed in mature pine stands makes it an ecological indicator species for habitat health and quality. Its narrow niche requirements likely led to the extinction of its Bahamas populations following the clear-cutting of much native pine forest, along with devastating hurricane damage in recent years.

The Brown-headed Nuthatch is one of the two smallest species in its mostly Northern hemisphere dwelling genus and family. Its brown-capped plumage is not shared by any other nuthatch.

DISTRIBUTION

POLIOPTILA CAERULEA

BLUE-GRAY GNATCATCHER

PASSERIFORMES

ADULT BIRD SIZE RANGE
4–4½ in (10–11 cm)

ORDER ~ Passeriformes

FAMILY ~ Polioptilidae

BREEDING RANGE ~ Temperate North America, Central America

BREEDING HABITAT ~ Deciduous woodlands, from scrub to mature forest, often near water or other habitat edges

NEST TYPE AND PLACEMENT ~ Deep, open cup, built from grasses, cobwebs, and lichens; attached to top of branches and limbs of shrubs and trees with dense canopy

CONSERVATION STATUS ~ Least concern

This is a small and mostly migratory songbird, and the northernmost representative of a typically tropical, New World lineage. Once it returns from the wintering grounds, pairs of females and males can form within just one day. The two sexes contribute equally to all aspects of parental care, from nest construction, through incubation and the feeding of the nestlings. In warmer regions, where there is time for second broods, the male constructs the bulk of the second nest while the female completes the first breeding bout.

Although the geographic range of this species has been expanding northward in recent years, so has its exposure to the negative effects of brood parasitism by Brown-headed Cowbirds. With the large and intensively begging cowbird chick in the nest of the gnatcatcher, the host's own small chicks invariably starve to death.

The Blue-Gray Gnatcatcher is bluer as male, with a prominent black unibrow across its forehead, and grayer as female or juvenile. Altogether, it is one of the lightest songbird species in North America.

DISTRIBUTION

SIALIA MEXICANA

WESTERN BLUEBIRD

PASSERIFORMES

ADULT BIRD SIZE RANGE
6–7 in (15–18 cm)

ORDER ~ Passeriformes

FAMILY ~ Turdidae

BREEDING RANGE ~ Western, coastal North America

BREEDING HABITAT ~ Open woodlands, gallery forests, riparian areas

NEST TYPE AND PLACEMENT ~ In natural tree cavities, old woodpecker holes, or
nestboxes; nest cup lined with dry grasses, rootlets,
feathers, and hair

CONSERVATION STATUS ~ Least concern

The bright blue feathers of Western Bluebirds are not only pleasant to look at against the dry grasses of its open woodland habitat, they also convey critical information about each individual. For example, the bluer the head, the older the male; and the larger his rufous breast patch, the healthier he is. Pairs are socially monogamous, with helpers—often mature sons of the resident pair—contributing to territory defense and feeding the young.

Western Bluebirds can plan for the future. In the fall, the dominant male decides whether to tolerate independent young (who may later become helpers) or to chase them away from the family territory, based on the potential availability of a critical winter food resource: mistletoe berries. Mistletoes produce berries only later in the year, so he apparently assesses the presence of mistletoe bunches alone: when scientists removed mistletoe bunches in the summer, the young were less likely to remain through the winter.

The Western Bluebird is a pleasant mix of rusty-orange and indigo-blue plumage patterns, with the hues decreasing in brightness from the males, to the somewhat duller females, and the even duller juveniles.

DISTRIBUTION

HYLOCICHLA MUSTELINA

WOOD THRUSH

PASSERIFORMES

ADULT BIRD SIZE RANGE
7–8½ in (18–22 cm)

ORDER ~ Passeriformes

FAMILY ~ Turdidae

BREEDING RANGE ~ Temperate eastern and central North America

BREEDING HABITAT ~ Mature, deciduous and mixed forests, with a dense shrub layer

NEST TYPE AND PLACEMENT ~ Cup nest in a forked branch, or near the trunk; bulky and made of twigs, bark, and straw, lined with leaves and grasses

CONSERVATION STATUS ~ Least concern

Admired by many as the bird singing the most beautiful melodies in North America, the song of the Wood Thrush is a sure sign of spring and the onset of the arrival of migrant birds from the neotropics. The flute-like quality of this bird's vocalizations is produced by the syrinx, the unique apparatus that allows songbirds to generate two different voices, at two different pitches, that are heard as one combined sound by the listener.

Pairs of Wood Thrush remain together on the nesting territory during the days leading up to egg laying, when the female is fertile; this means that both the female and the male have little chance to engage in extramarital affairs. Accordingly, in one study, more than 90 percent of the young were sired by both members of the resident pair, making this one of the most genetically faithful songbird species.

The Wood Thrush is a size and color monomorphic species, with heavy chest spots unparalleled by the more finely spotted thrushes in its own genus. The juvenile has additional spots on its back and wings.

DISTRIBUTION

DUMETELLA CAROLINENSIS

GRAY CATBIRD

PASSERIFORMES

ADULT BIRD SIZE RANGE
8½–9½ in (21–24 cm)

ORDER ~ Passeriformes

FAMILY ~ Mimidae

BREEDING RANGE ~ Temperate eastern and central North America;
introduced to Bermuda

BREEDING HABITAT ~ Dense shrubs, open areas with vines and thickets,
city parks and suburban backyards

NEST TYPE AND PLACEMENT ~ Cup nest in the center of dense foliage in a brush,
small trees, or in vines; made of sticks and twigs,
lined with rootlets and grasses

CONSERVATION STATUS ~ Least concern

The Gray Catbird lays some of the brightest and most intensely colored eggs among birds, with a uniform shiny green hue. But few people or predators ever see these eggs because the nest is well hidden deep in the dense foliage of low shrubs. The male stands guard over the nest while the incubating female is off to feed herself. Catbirds are also known to peck and remove eggs from active nests of other birds breeding near their own nest.

Together with mockingbirds and thrashers, the Gray Catbird belongs to the New World family Mimidae, which is known for its mimetic, variable, and continuously changing vocal displays. Gray Catbirds are among the handful of songbird species that are frequently parasitized by Brown-headed Cowbirds; however, the catbirds have evolved to recognize and eliminate a foreign egg from the nest by piercing and grasping it, then tossing or flying away with it.

The Gray Catbird is not a relative of Australian catbirds, but instead related to other singing experts, including thrashers and mockingbirds. Its uniform gray body plumage is shared by both sexes and with juveniles.

DISTRIBUTION

STURNUS VULGARIS

COMMON STARLING

PASSERIFORMES

ADULT BIRD SIZE RANGE
7½–9 in (19–23 cm)

ORDER ~ Passeriformes

FAMILY ~ Sturnidae

BREEDING RANGE ~ Europe and northwestern Asia; introduced and
broadly established on other continents

BREEDING HABITAT ~ Open forests, parklands, orchards, city parks

NEST TYPE AND PLACEMENT ~ Untidy bowl or cup nest, in a natural or artificial
cavity, box, tractor engine, or other enclosed space;
made from straw, grasses, and twigs, lined with
feathers, wool, and soft leaves

CONSERVATION STATUS ~ Least concern

The Common, or European, Starling is a nearly ubiquitous songbird. Its raspy but melodious song can be heard on each inhabited continent, either because it is a native species or because introduced populations have been established. The starling as an invasive species represents a severe danger for many other birds, as they are aggressive and successfully destroy or evict other native birds' nesting attempts from highly contested natural cavities in the forest.

Once a pair of starlings is settled to breed, the sexes share incubation and feeding duties equitably. However, if a female settles and mates with a male who is already mated, this secondary female will only receive paternal assistance if the first female's nesting attempt fails. Female starlings also often lay eggs parasitically in other starlings' nests, especially when the parasites themselves have lost their own nest to predation during the laying period.

The Common Starling is one of the most successful invaders of the avian world. Its green and purple, iridescent plumage is shared by the sexes, but males flaunt their longer and looser throat feathers during mate attraction.

DISTRIBUTION

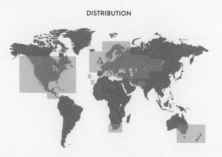

MOTACILLA ALBA

WHITE WAGTAIL

PASSERIFORMES

ADULT BIRD SIZE RANGE
6½–7½ in (17–19 cm)

ORDER ~ Passeriformes

FAMILY ~ Motacillidae

BREEDING RANGE ~ Northwestern Africa, temperate and subarctic Eurasia

BREEDING HABITAT ~ Open, flat grasslands, riverine corridors, coastal plateaus, subalpine clearings, parklands

NEST TYPE AND PLACEMENT ~ In a cavity, crevice, hole in the wall, or under an overhang in a soil bank; bulky nest of leaves, stems, and rootlets, lined with plant fluff, hair, and fur

CONSERVATION STATUS ~ Least concern

The White Wagtail is a charismatic species, whose characteristic pied plumage and distinctive tail motions are familiar to many people, especially because these birds often migrate through city parks alongside rivers and streams. This wagtail maintains territories both summer and winter. In the winter, a satellite juvenile or an adult female is allowed to join the male's territory, whereas in the summer, the breeding pair together maintains an all-purpose range, used for both feeding and nesting.

The pair chooses the nesting site together; the male may lead the female to suitable crevices, often carrying a piece of nesting material, while the female inspects each site closely. Once a site is accepted, the nest is built by both members of the pair, and incubation is also shared. After the eggs hatch, both parents begin their frequent delivery of arthropod prey to the nestlings, but the mother may stay behind after each feeding to brood the chicks to keep them warm.

The White Wagtail is a distinctively patterned species, sporting white, gray, or black regions across its body, with different geographic population varying in the extent of black on the crown, face, throat, and/or back.

DISTRIBUTION

SNOW BUNTING

PASSERIFORMES

ADULT BIRD SIZE RANGE
6–7 in (15–18 cm)

ORDER ~ Passeriformes

FAMILY ~ Calcariidae

BREEDING RANGE ~ Arctic North America and Eurasia

BREEDING HABITAT ~ Treeless tundra, rocky fields, bare mountain tops

NEST TYPE AND PLACEMENT ~ Deep inside a rock crevice or fissure; open cup of moss and grass, lined with fine grasses, rootlets, hair, and feathers

CONSERVATION STATUS ~ Least concern

The Snow Bunting's white plumage in the winter serves both for camouflage in the snow and to reflect body heat back into the bird. Together with the much larger, and black, Common Raven, this bunting is the most northerly wintering songbird. Wintering far north saves time for the males, who arrive several weeks before the female to set up and defend breeding territories in the high Arctic. The value of each territory depends on the availability of rock crevices for nesting. Cavity nesting protects the buntings from predators that use vision to hunt in the open, treeless Arctic breeding grounds.

When the females arrive, showing off the feasible nest sites to the potential mate is a part of the males' courtship displays. Once a pair bond is formed, nest building can begin. If there is an old nest in the crevice, the female may reuse it as a base to build her new nest. The female alone incubates the eggs and broods the hatchlings, but the male joins in to provision the growing young.

The Snow Bunting is a circumpolar species of the Artic regions. It becomes sexually dichromatic for the reproductive season only, with the males displaying a blacker back than the rusty back of the females.

DISTRIBUTION

SETOPHAGA TIGRINA

CAPE MAY WARBLER

PASSERIFORMES

MALE

FEMALE

ADULT BIRD SIZE RANGE
4½–5½ in (12–14 cm)

ORDER ~ Passeriformes

FAMILY ~ Parulidae

BREEDING RANGE ~ Boreal North America

BREEDING HABITAT ~ Coniferous forests with unbroken canopy

NEST TYPE AND PLACEMENT ~ Bulky cup of mosses, twigs, spruce needles, and bark strips, lined with rootlets, plant fluff, hair, and feathers; placed high in a spruce or fir tree

CONSERVATION STATUS ~ Least concern

To attract a female to the breeding territory, the male Cape May Warbler sings and hops around her with his wings erect and rigid. He also follows her closely during nest construction, although he does not assist. The female stays on the nest tightly during incubation, and is reluctant to flush unless danger is imminent. The pair feeds the chicks a mostly larval diet through fledging. Perhaps because of the remote breeding habitat of this species, relatively little else is known about the breeding cycle and paternal care patterns.

This is another warbler species that was named after its first collecting site, where it was not seen again for another 100 years. A resident of the boreal coniferous forests of Canada, this species is a specialist feeder on caterpillars, which have characteristic eruption cycles, closely followed by the warbler's own population size fluctuations.

The Cape May Warbler is a small New World warbler, related to other colorful and sexually dichromatic congeneric species across the Americas. Its Latin name comes from its striped chest patterns across both sexes.

DISTRIBUTION

BLACK-THROATED BLUE WARBLER

PASSERIFORMES

MALE

FEMALE

ADULT BIRD SIZE RANGE
4½–5 in (11–13 cm)

ORDER ~ Passeriformes

FAMILY ~ Parulidae

BREEDING RANGE ~ Eastern North America and the Appalachian Mountains

BREEDING HABITAT ~ Large, mature tracks of hardwood and mixed coniferous forests

NEST TYPE AND PLACEMENT ~ Open cup, made from strips of bark, held together with spider web and saliva; placed in the fork of a low shrub

CONSERVATION STATUS ~ Least concern

The Black-throated Blue Warbler breeds in the temperate forests of eastern North America, and winters on islands of the Caribbean. While many studies have been conducted on the annual dynamics of this species' breeding populations in the north, as well as the wintering populations in the tropics, it has been difficult to understand its migratory pathways and connectivity. However, scientists have now connected these warblers' northern breeding populations to Cuba and Jamaica, and the Appalachian populations to Hispaniola and Puerto Rico.

The female produces a characteristic chip sound while she collects nesting material, making it easier for the male to follow her during nest building. Despite mate-guarding by the male, many females mate with neighbors, who then sire some of the young in nests for which they do not provide paternal care.

The Black-throated Blue Warbler is a charismatic and colorful inhabitant of montane Eastern North America; the male (top) and, to some extent, the female sport a white wing patch that makes them noticeable from long distances.

DISTRIBUTION

MYIOBORUS PICTUS

PAINTED REDSTART

PASSERIFORMES

ADULT BIRD SIZE RANGE
5–6 in (13–15 cm)

ORDER ~ Passeriformes

FAMILY ~ Parulidae

BREEDING RANGE ~ Southwestern North America, northern
Central America

BREEDING HABITAT ~ Open and dry pine and oak woodlands

NEST TYPE AND PLACEMENT ~ Open cup, made of coarse grasses and pine
needles; placed on the ground, in rock walls,
or on sloping terrain

CONSERVATION STATUS ~ Least concern

Unlike some other wood warblers, the female Painted Redstart also sings, and vocalizations by both sexes form important components of courtship displays. Once the pair bond is cemented, the pair inspects suitable nest sites together, and then the female brings construction materials to the chosen site. The female completes the nest on her own, incubates the eggs, and broods the chicks; both parents feed the nestlings, however, typically in equal frequencies.

This bright red, black, and white warbler and its neotropical relatives are not related to the redstarts of Eurasia, and are only distantly related to the parulid American Redstart; thus, sometimes they are called "whitestarts" to avoid confusion with the other lineages. Whitestart is a particularly appropriate name because the white patches against the black feathers of the tail and wings are used as flashy visual devices to scare and flush insects from hiding.

The Painted Redstart is a sexually monochromatic species, with both sexes sharing the stark black and bright red and white plumage patterns. The juveniles, in turn, are paler and do not yet display red on their feathers.

DISTRIBUTION

SPIZELLOIDES ARBOREA

AMERICAN TREE SPARROW

PASSERIFORMES

ADULT BIRD SIZE RANGE
5½–6¾ in (14–17 cm)

ORDER ~ Passeriformes

FAMILY ~ Emberizidae

BREEDING RANGE ~ Arctic and subarctic North America

BREEDING HABITAT ~ Open tundra, shrubby areas, boreal forest edges

NEST TYPE AND PLACEMENT ~ Open cup, made of mosses, grasses, bark shreds, and twigs, lined with finer grasses and downy feathers; placed on or near the ground, in a tussock of grass

CONSERVATION STATUS ~ Least concern

This species is familiar throughout the North American temperate zone as a common winter-resident species, but its breeding range is far north, past the wide band of boreal pine forests. The males advertise their territory by loud song in the open tundra, and the females make decisions about pair bonding soon after they arrive on these breeding grounds. Females select the nest site, incubate the eggs, and brood the chicks, while the male often visits the nest, but he does not contribute until the chicks require regular feeding visits.

Lacking teeth, birds must soften foods like seeds before digestion; to do this they swallow and accumulate grit and small pebbles in their crop where the seeds are ground up. Nestling birds are fed grit by the parents; in American Tree Sparrows, grit first shows up in the crop at about three days after hatching.

The American Tree Sparrow is a long-tailed, chunky-bodied, and rusty-capped bird, with a prominent dark chest spot and a bitonal beak, featuring a consistently black upper and yellow lower mandible.

DISTRIBUTION

EMBERIZA CITRINELLA

YELLOWHAMMER

PASSERIFORMES

ADULT BIRD SIZE RANGE
6–6½ in (15–17 cm)

ORDER ~ Passeriformes

FAMILY ~ Emberizidae

BREEDING RANGE ~ Europe and northwestern Asia; introduced to
New Zealand

BREEDING HABITAT ~ Open scrub, shrubby grasslands, farms and pastures

NEST TYPE AND PLACEMENT ~ In hedges, scrub, and on the ground in sloping
ditches; open cup, made of twigs and sticks, lined
with woven grasses and rootlets

CONSERVATION STATUS ~ Least concern

Yellowhammers are colorful and melodious broadcasters of spring, but recent changes in agricultural practices have led to consistent declines in many populations. For example, in Britain shrinking populations have been linked to losses in hedges and other shrubby areas around large cultivated fields. These trends may be countered, however, by the growing number of organic farms, which are smaller in size and often surrounded by shrubby boundaries.

Surprisingly for a small insectivorous and open-cup nesting passerine, Yellowhammers are rarely parasitized by Common Cuckoos, despite their overlapping ranges. One explanation is that this potential host species is an acute egg discriminator. Blue, non-mimetic eggs introduced experimentally to nests were nearly all rejected, and even a third of mimetic eggs taken from other Yellowhammer nests were rejected. This implies that Yellowhammers might once have been cuckoo-hosts, but any parasite specializing on them is now probably extinct.

The Yellowhammer is a sexually dichromatic species, with bright yellows in males replaced by paler greenish tones in females and juveniles. Still, it is not its plumage but its songs that broadcast its presence most loudly.

DISTRIBUTION

PIRANGA OLIVACEA

SCARLET TANAGER

PASSERIFORMES

MALE

FEMALE

ADULT BIRD SIZE RANGE
6¼–6½ in (16–17 cm)

ORDER ~ Passeriformes

FAMILY ~ Cardinalidae

BREEDING RANGE ~ Eastern and central North America

BREEDING HABITAT ~ Large tracts of mature deciduous and mixed forests

NEST TYPE AND PLACEMENT ~ Loosely woven, shallow pan of twigs, grasses, stalks, strips of bark, rootlets, and pine needles, lined with grasses, rootlets, vine tendrils, and plant fibers; placed high, near the terminus of a horizontal branch

CONSERVATION STATUS ~ Least concern

Formerly associated with the neotropical tanager family, this flaming red and coal-black bird is now classified as a relative of cardinals and their allies. A long-distance migrant between South and North America, the males arrive before the females, and establish their breeding territories through song and flight. The females quickly select their mates, and nest building can be well on its way just one week after the females return.

The male occasionally follows the female while she gathers nesting materials, but she alone constructs the nest and incubates the eggs. Some males feed their mate on the nest, but others do not and the female will leave the nest periodically to feed herself. After the eggs hatch, the male begins food delivery to the nest, often while the female is still brooding the hatchlings to keep them warm before their feathers grow in and their own thermoregulatory systems become fully functional.

The Scarlet Tanager is a species with delayed plumage maturation, which means that young males, even though sexually mature already, show a complex transition between their greenish female-like juvenile and red and black adult male-like feather colors.

DISTRIBUTION

INDIGO BUNTING

PASSERIFORMES

ADULT BIRD SIZE RANGE
4½–5 in (12–13 cm)

ORDER ~ Passeriformes

FAMILY ~ Cardinalidae

BREEDING RANGE ~ Eastern and southern North America

BREEDING HABITAT ~ Open thickets, forest edges, shrubby grasslands

NEST TYPE AND PLACEMENT ~ Open cup of woven leaves, grasses, stems, bark strips, and spider web, lined with thin grasses, rootlets, thistledown, and deer hair; placed in a crotch or fork in a low shrub or tree

CONSERVATION STATUS ~ Least concern

The male Indigo Bunting's bright blue spring color is an indication of advanced age; first-time breeding males often carry some brown-gray feathers, a phenomenon known as delayed plumage maturation. Apparently, young birds use plumage color to assess the suitability of tutors for song learning. Older males' songs are more likely to be learned by young neighbors; the songs of bluer young males' songs also are more often copied than those of browner young males.

The Indigo Bunting is heavily parasitized by Brown-headed Cowbirds in the forest edge habitats where both species prefer to breed. In the bunting's small nest cup, the fast-growing cowbird chick can marginalize, and even accidentally evict, some of the host young. Also, the cowbird's intensive begging attracts not only preferential provisioning from the foster parents over their own genetic young, but also risks the parasite's own survival chances by attracting predators cued in by its loud begging calls.

The Indigo Bunting is one of six brightly colored species in its genus, the male molting into its namesake plumage for mating. Juveniles and females, as well as non-breeding males, are all cryptic brown.

DISTRIBUTION

AGELAIUS PHOENICEUS

RED-WINGED BLACKBIRD

PASSERIFORMES

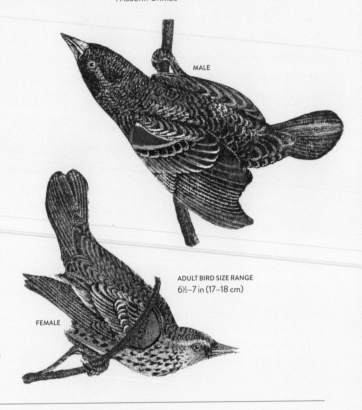

MALE

ADULT BIRD SIZE RANGE
6½–7 in (17–18 cm)

FEMALE

ORDER ~ Passeriformes

FAMILY ~ Icteridae

BREEDING RANGE ~ North America, Central America, western
Caribbean

BREEDING HABITAT ~ Wetlands, marshes, thickets, fallow fields, roadside
ditches, parklands

NEST TYPE AND PLACEMENT ~ Open cup, placed low among reeds and other marsh
vegetation, but also in shrubs; made of leaves, wood
strips, and mud, lined with fine, dry grasses

CONSERVATION STATUS ~ Least concern

The Red-winged Blackbird is likely the most numerous passerine bird in all of North America. The male's red and yellow shoulder patch, contrasting with his black plumage, is a characteristic sight along highways, rural roads, farms, salt marshes, city parks, and river walks; his call of "conk-a-reeee" is a typical sound of spring. In the fall, million-strong flocks of blackbirds, and other icterids, move, feed, and roost together.

To impress the female, the male blackbird sings and bows to her; he is able to project his voice directly at the female watching this courtship display. This blackbird is a territorial, colonial breeder, with males defending territories containing suitable nesting sites. The safest nesting sites tend to be in marshes where some males may have multiple females nesting on their territories. The females incubate the eggs alone, while the male patrols the territory, alarm-calling, and mobbing predators (including passing humans) to defend the nests.

The Red-winged Blackbird is part of a four-species complex that all display bright red shoulder patches used for aggressive and sexual displays by the males. The female redwing is browner and cryptic in reedbeds.

DISTRIBUTION

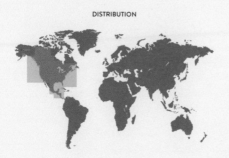

ICTERUS SPURIUS

ORCHARD ORIOLE

PASSERIFORMES

ADULT BIRD SIZE RANGE
6–7 in (15–18 cm)

ORDER ~ Passeriformes

FAMILY ~ Icteridae

BREEDING RANGE ~ Eastern and southern North America

BREEDING HABITAT ~ Open woodlands, riparian corridors, wooded marshes, flood plain forests

NEST TYPE AND PLACEMENT ~ Hanging pouch, made of woven grass, lined with finer grasses, plant down, wool, and feathers; hung from the fork of a branch, near the tip, on a small or medium-sized tree

CONSERVATION STATUS ~ Least concern

The Orchard Oriole is a true neotropical bird that happens to breed in the north temperate zone; the breeding season lasts from May to July, but once the chicks have fledged, by mid-July, many adults quickly take off on their southwardly migration. Thus, nearly three-quarters of the annual cycle of this species is spent outside the breeding range.

There are at least three distinct plumage morphs of Orchard Orioles: females, second-year males, and older males. This poses the question why younger males should display their age so visibly: both types of males arrive at the breeding ground at the same time, and display to females, who generally choose an older male. Females move through territories of different males, assessing their song and plumage patterns, and take several days to settle into a pair bond. Nest building begins a few days later and the female can complete the nest in under a week. She starts laying her clutch the next day.

The Orchard Oriole is a prominently bitonal species, with adult males sporting black or chestnut and females showing greenish or black color patches. The sexes use both their colorful plumage and distinct calls to display to each other during courtship.

DISTRIBUTION

FRINGILLA COELEBS

COMMON CHAFFINCH

PASSERIFORMES

ADULT BIRD SIZE RANGE
5½–6½ in (14–16 cm)

ORDER ~ Passeriformes

FAMILY ~ Fringillidae

BREEDING RANGE ~ Western Asia, Europe, north Africa

BREEDING HABITAT ~ Open woodlands, forest edges, city parks,
and backyards

NEST TYPE AND PLACEMENT ~ Open-cup nest in a tree fork; exterior covered with
moss or lichen, interior lined with grasses and fibers,
matted together with wool and cobwebs

CONSERVATION STATUS ~ Least concern

In western Europe the Chaffinch is the most common finch. It sings a melodious tune to delineate its breeding territory and to attract the female. It is no surprise that English settlers arriving two centuries ago in places as far away as New Zealand insisted on bringing breeding pairs of this familiar songbird with them for release and propagation in the new colonies. In the absence of most of their typical mammalian and reptilian nest predators common in Eurasia, Chaffinches introduced to New Zealand flourished and today they are some of the commonest and loudest urban and parkland birds.

Chaffinches possess regional song differences generated by the process of cultural evolution, whereby young birds learn to imitate closely, but not perfectly, some older tutors, and also invent new song variants on their own. These variants are then passed down to the next generation through imitative learning.

The Common Chaffinch is a sexually dichromatic species, with the males showing variable reddish-pink body plumage and a blueish-gray head region. Still, it is the male's song that pinpoints him in the forest most prominently.

DISTRIBUTION

EURASIAN BULLFINCH

PASSERIFORMES

ADULT BIRD SIZE RANGE
6–6½ in (15–17 cm)

ORDER ~ Passeriformes

FAMILY ~ Fringillidae

BREEDING RANGE ~ Temperate Eurasia

BREEDING HABITAT ~ Coniferous and mixed forests, woodland corridors, parks, and gardens

NEST TYPE AND PLACEMENT ~ Open-cup nest, made of twigs, mosses, and lichens, lined with rootlets and hair; built inside the canopy of a tree, or in dense foliage, or in a large bush

CONSERVATION STATUS ~ Least concern

The male of this bullfinch is brightly colored, with a handsome blue-gray back, and a peach-pink chest. Its unique chest coloration is derived from the carotenoid pigmentation of the berries and fruits it consumes during the molt. In captivity, these yellow to rosy red pigments must be supplemented in the diet to prevent fading of these plumage patterns.

The male Eurasian Bullfinch is also unique among fringillid finches in that its gonads, the internal testes, are the smallest compared to other species, representing less than a third of 1 percent of its total body mass. Furthermore, the sperm produced by these small testes is highly variable in shape and speed. Taking these two factors together, scientists have predicted that the strength of sexual competition between males is fairly relaxed. Accordingly, instead of seeking reproductive opportunities elsewhere, males keep themselves busy assisting the female to incubate the eggs and feed the chicks.

The Eurasian Bullfinch is a chunky, heavy-beaked, and color-dimorphic species, with an unmistakable peachy breast of the male. Yet, unlike in many other related finches, both sexes contribute to incubation and look after the nestlings.

DISTRIBUTION

TAENIOPYGIA GUTTATA

ZEBRA FINCH

PASSERIFORMES

FEMALE

MALE

ADULT BIRD SIZE RANGE
4–4½ in (10–11 cm)

ORDER ~ Passeriformes

FAMILY ~ Estrildidae

BREEDING RANGE ~ Inland Australia, Indonesian archipelago

BREEDING HABITAT ~ Grassland, thickets, open forests, usually close to water; also artificial watering holes, farmland, and lawns

NEST TYPE AND PLACEMENT ~ Domed nest made of hay, stems, and fine twigs, lined with finer grasses, wool, and feathers

CONSERVATION STATUS ~ Least concern

Zebra Finches in the wild often initiate breeding when encountering reliable access to water; in captivity, with unlimited access to water, these birds are ready to breed year-round. The socially monogamous pair bond, which lasts for a lifetime in captivity, is also present in the wild and represents a genetically faithful mating relationship; all eggs laid by a female are sired by the father with whom she is paired.

Zebra Finches are the avian equivalent of the white laboratory rat; due to the ease with which they can be bred in captivity, they are the subject of numerous genetic, morphological, developmental, neurophysiological, and behavioral studies. The full genome of the Zebra Finch has now been sequenced and made public, allowing researchers to investigate the genetic basis for developmental similarities between the ways male Zebra Finches learn to imitate their father's song and human children learn to babble and then speak their parents' language.

The Zebra Finch is a popular cage bird, with the sexes distinguished by the male's orange cheek patches and zebra striped neck pattern. Females, however, pay close attention to the bright red beak during courtship.

DISTRIBUTION

GLOSSARY

Altricial The state of a chick's development when it needs to remain in the nest for prolonged periods as it is typically naked, blind, and depends on the parents fully for food.

Brood patch A vascularized patch of featherless, bare skin that forms on the belly of many incubating birds during the breeding season, to allow efficient transfer of heat from adult to eggs.

Brooding An adult using its body and plumage to cover the chicks and keep them warm in or outside the nest.

Commensal Coexisting with another organism without harm or benefit.

Consortship Escorting, following, and keeping near another individual, usually referring to behavior associated with a seasonal or long-term pair bond, but could also be seen in other mating or social groups.

Conspecific Of the same species.

Crepuscular Active at low light, including dusk and dawn.

Crop A muscular compartment just past the throat of a bird that helps to grind and break up hard foods, including seeds.

Cryptic Hidden against a background.

Cryptic species Two species that appear similar in morphology but possess other evolutionary (genetic, behavioral, etc.) differences that are the result of separate evolutionary paths.

Dabbling duck Collective common name for duck species that feed on or just below the surface of a pond, lake, river, or the sea; dipping their heads underwater.

Delayed plumage maturation The state of being reproductively ready but not yet having attained adult plumage.

Embryogenesis The formation and development of a fertilized egg into an embryonic organism.

Endemic Occurring only within the confines of a specific locality, including islands, countries, continents, or other geographic regions.

Fecal sac Excrement produced by nestlings, enclosed in a gelatinous membrane, easily carried in the beak and removed from the nest by parents.

Fledging The act of young departing from the nest.

Fledgling Chicks that have grown their initial flight feathers and left the nest, whether they are able to fly or not. Some fledglings still depend on parental care and feeding. See Nestling.

Helpers at the nest Individuals other than the breeding pair who provide parental care including incubation, feeding, brooding, and/or protection of a nest site. Helpers in birds are often, but not always, young from a previous brood by the pair.

Hybridization Breeding between individuals from different species.

Immaculate Clear, having no spots.

Incubation The act of warming eggs to raise the internal temperature sufficiently high for embryonic development.

Kleptoparasite A bird that obtains food or prey by stealing it from another bird.

Lek Group of same-sex individuals displaying together to attract the opposite sex for mating.

Long-distance migrant A migrant bird engaging in a journey that takes it to another continent or across marine bodies of water.

Maculation Spotting, speckling, blotching, or other patterning against a uniform background on an egg.

Mimetic Resembling (or mimicking) a model in appearance. Some brood parasitic bird species lay eggs that have evolved to mimic the appearance of the eggs of its host.

Natal A term referring to the locality where a bird hatched.

Nestling A chick that has not yet left the nest.

Nocturnal Being active during nighttime.

Obligate Required, involuntary, or inflexible; generally under genetic control. A behavior that is present in all individuals of the same species.

Pair bond The social attachment between a male and female for reproductive purposes.

Philopatry The tendency to return to the same place; for example natal philopatry refers to returning to the site of the nest where the bird was hatched.

Passerine Birds of the order Passeriformes, commonly known as perching birds. This order makes up roughly half of modern avian species.

Pelagic Of open water; the region of a lake or an ocean which is neither close to the shore, nor the bottom.

Polyandry A breeding system with one female mating and producing young with multiple males.

Polygyny A breeding system with one male mating and producing young with multiple females.

Polymorphism Refers to a trait that has variation within a species.

Precocial The state of development of a chick such that it is ready to leave the nest soon after it hatches and dries; it may or may not be able to feed itself.

Raptor A bird of prey.

Ratites A group of flightless birds native to the southern hemisphere; includes ostriches, emus, rheas, kiwis, and the extinct moas and elephantbirds.

Regurgitate To bring up food previously swallowed; a common method for parents to provide food to dependent young.

Sexual dimorphism Differences in size, appearance, and/or behavior between females and males.

Suboscine Refers to the lineage of Passerine birds without a functional syrinx; includes tyrant flycatchers and antbirds.

Synchrony Coordinated timing within an individual nest or between nests in a population; for example, a female may delay incubation of eggs laid on different days, so that they hatch on the same day.

Syrinx The vocal organ of birds, which is analogous to a mammal's larynx, but without vocal cords.

Volant Able to fly.

RESOURCES

BOOKS

General
Birds: A Complete Guide to their Biology and Behaviour, Jonathan Elphick (Natural History Museum, 2016)

Handbook of Bird Biology, Cornell Laboratory of Ornithology, Eds. Irby J. Lovette and John W. Fitzpatrick (3rd edition, 2016, Wiley Press).

Life-Size Birds, Rob Read and Paul Sterry (Collins, 2016)

Ornithology, Frank B. Gill, Richard O. Prum, Scott Robinson (4th edition, 2019, W H Freeman)

There are also many thorough and helpful local guide books written about birds, their nests and eggs.

SCIENTIFIC JOURNALS

To read about the latest discoveries in ornithology, behavioral biology, and evolutionary history, many primary scientific journals provide summaries or instant peeks into their latest content through their websites; readers who would like to gain access to the full article may do so through institutional libraries or personal subscriptions, or (the best-kept secret in academic publishing!) simply by sending a quick email to the author(s) of the article, requesting a personal PDF copy of the work. The following list of scientific journals is not complete, but will be helpful to get started:

General biological coverage
Animal Behaviour; Behavioral Ecology; Behavioral Ecology & Sociobiology; Behaviour; Current Biology; Ecography; Ecology; Ethology; Ethology Ecology & Evolution; Evolution; Evolutionary Ecology Research; Functional Ecology; Journal of Animal Ecology; Journal of Evolutionary Biology; Journal of Experimental Biology; Nature; Nature Communications; Oecologia; PLoS ONE; Proceedings of the National Academy of Sciences of the USA; Proceedings of the Royal Society of London B; The Royal Society Journal Interface; Science.

Specialist ornithological journals
The Auk: Ornithological Advances; The Condor: Ornithological Applications; The Emu; The Ibis; Journal of Avian Biology; Journal of Field Ornithology; Journal of Ornithology; Notornis; and the Wilson Journal of Ornithology.

SOME USEFUL WEBSITES

audubon.org
The website of the National Audubon Society, which works to protect birds and their habitats.

birdsoftheworld.org
This is a collection of all bird species curated by the Cornell Laboratory of Ornithology.

birdlife.org
The website of BirdLife International, a bird conservation organisation. Use the Data Zone to find out more about global species.

bto.org
The British Trust for Ornithology encourages birdwatchers to gather and share information to help understand birds and monitor changes in their populations.

COLLECTIONS

To view preserved specimens of birds, these museums provide some of the most extensive collections - both on display and behind the scenes.

The Field Museum of Natural History (Chicago, USA), the Western Foundation of Vertebrate Zoology (near Los Angeles, USA), the Natural History Museum (Tring, Hertfordshire, UK), the Peabody Museum of Natural History (New Haven, USA), University Museum of Zoology (Cambridge, UK), the Museum of Comparative Zoology (Cambridge, USA), and many others. Each of these museums has its own web site, with information about current exhibits and visiting hours.

INDEX OF SPECIES BY COMMON NAME

INDEX OF SPECIES BY SCIENTIFIC NAME

ACKNOWLEDGMENTS

The author and publishers are grateful to John Bates and
Barbara Becker of the Field Museum in Chicago for their
work as consultant editors of *The Book of Eggs*, from which
this book is derived.

PICTURE CREDITS
All original engravings are courtesy of Biodiversity Heritage Library
apart from the following:
Shutterstock/ Antonio Abrignani 58; Hein Nouwens 22, 70, 72.